WITHDRAWN

D1486901

Living Through the Older Years

CHARLES ASBURY FISHER

Living
Through the Older Years

PROCEEDINGS OF THE
CHARLES A. FISHER MEMORIAL INSTITUTE
ON AGING

EDITED BY
CLARK TIBBITTS

WITH A FOREWORD BY
EVERETT J. SOOP

ANN ARBOR
UNIVERSITY OF MICHIGAN PRESS
1949

COPYRIGHT
1949
BY THE UNIVERSITY
OF MICHIGAN

HQ
1061
C 5

618.97
C47l

DEDICATED TO THE MEMORY OF

CHARLES ASBURY FISHER

DIRECTOR OF THE UNIVERSITY OF MICHIGAN
EXTENSION SERVICE
1937 – 1948

Foreword

THROUGHOUT HIS twenty-two years with the University of Michigan Extension Service and especially during the eleven years he served as Director, Dr. Charles A. Fisher established an enviable state and national record as a pioneer in adult education. Of a philosophical turn of mind, Dr. Fisher was constantly studying and thinking about the educational interests and needs of the adult population of his state and nation.

At least four years ago, in conversation with members of his staff, Dr. Fisher introduced the idea that the Extension Service should consider what it could do to assist adults to prepare for a more useful and satisfactory later maturity and old age. He was especially interested in the development of productive leadership in older people. At the time of his sudden death on March 30, 1948, he was an active participant in the University's first experimental program in problems of the aging. He also helped to formulate the initial plans for a conference the following summer. In tribute to his leadership, this conference was later named The Charles A. Fisher Memorial Institute on Aging.

Dr. Fisher always gave credit to persons who affected his thinking and planning of extension programs. It seems fitting, therefore, that mention be made of the persons he named at various times as having influenced his ideas on the development of programs for people in later maturity. They were, in addition to his family and staff, President Alexander G. Ruthven, the late Vice-President Emeritus James D. Bruce, Dr. Henry S. Curtis, Dr. and Mrs. Harry A. Overstreet, and Mr. Clark Tibbitts.

EVERETT J. SOOP
Director of the University Extension Service

Contents

Living Through the Older Years

Introduction

BY CLARK TIBBITTS

Director of the Institute for Human Adjustment

THIS LITTLE volume contains a collection of addresses given on the occasion of the first attempt in this country to hold a comprehensive conference on problems and adjustments in later maturity and old age. The conference itself was an experiment; the selection of discussion topics was not.

The Charles A. Fisher Memorial Institute on Aging, as the conference was called, was addressed to two groups of people: (1) professional workers such as adult education leaders, welfare workers, ministers, recreation workers, personnel workers, counselors, and public health nurses; and (2) middle-aged and older people alert enough to know that they can enjoy the later years if they understand themselves and the aging process and make suitable preparation.

At the time the Institute was announced there was no knowledge of the number of professional persons in the Middle West whose work brought them into contact with older people nor whether those who had such contact would be interested in it. There was experience to indicate that the conference would appeal to many people on a personal basis. During the spring of the year the University Extension Service and the Institute for Human Adjustment pioneered in offering a sixteen-week course covering topics of interest to older people. The immediate acceptance accorded the course showed that there is tremendous interest on the part of the aging and the aged in learning to live through the older years. Actually, the seven sessions of the Institute attracted a registered attendance of 332 persons, divided about equally between the professional and nonprofessional. Ninety-four agencies in twelve states and in Canada were represented by 194 staff members.

The point of view of those who planned the Institute was (1) that older people tend to be set aside and to set themselves aside from work, community participation, and family life, (2) that such retirement is largely involuntary because older people have the same basic desires and needs as they have had throughout their lives, (3) that both older people and the community as a whole are beginning to recognize that employability, interests, and the ability to plan one's own life continue much longer than has been supposed, and (4) that progress in individual and community adjustment to aging and an aging population depends, first, upon understanding and, second, upon both individual and community action.

The topics for the Institute, as for the course which preceded it, were selected to try to give a broad understanding of both the individual and social phases of these problems and, also, such suggestions as might be offered on the basis of present knowledge.

The first chapter, by Professor Ernest W. Burgess, offers a comprehensive statement of "The Growing Problem of Aging" in terms of numbers, activities, and social participation of older people and personal and social adjustment. He describes aging as a period of continued change requiring successive adjustments and, in this connection, develops the importance of considering the needs and wishes of the persons concerned. Finally, Professor Burgess describes various measures of adjustment and warns the community at large that it must give attention to the implications of such measures when they are applied.

The second chapter, contributed by Professor Carl V. Weller, was taken from the original course series. It is included in the present volume because of Professor Weller's superb demonstration of the life long, parallel processes of evolution and involution and because of the statements he makes regarding the dignity of aging and the potential contribution of older people.

In "The Personal Challenge of Aging" Dr. Edward Stieglitz covers some of the same ground in a different manner; he also discusses certain characteristics of the diseases of old age and places upon the individual the primary responsibility for maintaining a healthy, functioning organism. Dr. Wilma Donahue presents a scholarly review of "Changes in Psychological Processes" and, like Dr. Stieglitz, includes suggestions for those who wish to exercise some self-determination over the character of their own aging processes. She points out, too, that there may be a socially useful reason for the greater longevity of the cerebral functions than of the purely biological ones.

Dr. Moses Frohlich covers in succinct and careful fashion a large number of problems that affect the mental health of older people and of those associated with them. His chapter is concerned primarily with the effects of loss of job, decline in health, and loss of close associates, such as spouse, children, and friends. Preparation for old age is fundamental in his prescription for adjustment. Mrs. Patricia Rabinovitz considers a problem of adjustment, "Living Arrangements." Problems are examined with reference to living with relatives, living alone, and living in institutions. The chapter contains numerous suggestions for living contentedly through the older years.

Religion is important to at least one-half of all people and to a much greater proportion of older people. Professor Emeritus Leroy Waterman's vigorous chapter on "Religion and Religious Observance" includes a profound analysis of religion itself, a critical review of certain aspects of current religious observance, and a strong appeal to find individual satisfaction and the preservation of society through living according to the true religious principle.

"Aging Creatively" is the title of a stimulating chapter by psychologist Dr. George Lawton. Continued growth and creative activity are essential to successful aging. There are literally scores of activities that can be learned and pursued with great satisfaction whether or not the individual develops real expertness. Older people are challenged to use their imaginations.

The two chapters on economic problems of aging are

excellent statements of the related problems of employability of older workers and of the very complex economic problem of providing support for the aging. Commissioner Ewan Clague suggests increased employment for older workers in order that they may retain the feeling of social usefulness and to make it possible for them to have incomes sufficient for their needs. He describes the characteristics of workers who have passed middle age and offers suggestions for continuing employment.

Mr. Charles Kidd relates the income of older people to productivity, total national income, the needs of other dependent groups, and the effect on the economy. In addition, his chapter, "Economic Security for Older Persons," contains suggestions for broad revisions in government assistance and insurance plans.

The book concludes with a stirring appeal by Dr. Harry A. Overstreet for young people to prepare for old age and for older people to live intelligent, active, creative, and, hence, satisfying lives. It is hoped that the volume will, indeed, help the entire community to live more successfully throughout the life span.

I

The Growing Problem of Aging

By Ernest W. Burgess

*Ernest W. Burgess, Ph.D., is chairman of the Department of
Sociology at the University of Chicago. He is co-author of* Introduction to the Science of Sociology, The Workings of the Indeterminate Sentence Law and the Parole System in Illinois, Predicting
Success or Failure in Marriage, *and* The Family, *and is the author
of numerous other books and articles. He has been active in the
Social Science Research Council and is chairman of its Committee
on Problems and Policy and its Committee on Social Adjustment.
He has been editor of the* American Journal of Sociology *and president of the American Sociological Society and the Society for
Family Living. He is at present carrying on research in the field
of old-age adjustment.*

THE INSTITUTE on Aging is one of many indications of
growing interest in the problem of aging. It is noteworthy
in that it considers the many facets of the problems of later
maturity — biological, psychological, and sociological — in
relation to practical questions of mental health, religion,
leisure time, living arrangements, employment, and economic security.

It is high time that attention be paid to the problem of
aging both by the public and by medical, psychological, and
social scientists. There are several reasons why the problem
of aging is of growing concern.

First, the percentage of old persons in the population
of the United States is rapidly increasing. One hundred
years ago (1850) only 2.6 of the population was sixty-five
years of age and over, whereas in 1947 the percentage is
estimated at 7.5. The Census Bureau forecasts that by 1990,
13.1 per cent of all the inhabitants of this country will fall
in this age period. Without doubt the problem of aging is
one of increasing magnitude.

Second, the crux of the problem consists not in the increasing number of old persons but rather in the signifi-

7

cance of aging in our modern industrial society. In 1850 only 16 per cent of the people of the United States lived in communities of 2,500 population and over. In 1947, 59 per cent resided in urban areas. In this same year only 19 per cent of the American people lived on farms. This change of our country from a rural to an urban civilization has profound significance for the nature of the problem of aging.

Perhaps the significance of this change can best be appreciated by citing the case of the status of old persons among the Pennsylvania Amish, which represents, in a somewhat extreme form to be sure, the place of rural old persons in American society one hundred years ago. The Amish are selected for illustration because, to an extraordinary extent, they have succeeded in isolating themselves from the urbanizing influence of the environing society:

The Amish farmer is rooted to the soil and that is where he wants to remain. When the time comes to retire from active farming — usually when the youngest son or daughter marries — the aging parents move to a separate part of the house known as "Grossdawdy house." Sometimes this is an addition to the main house and sometimes it is a separate unit.

Grossdawdy does not retire from all work when he retires to his part of the house. He finds as much work outside as he cares to do. Grossmutter sews during the day for the children and grandchildren. This work keeps both of them healthily occupied as long as they are active. If they need attention younger members of the family are near. It is doubtful that old people anywhere are more contented than the occupants of the Grossdawdy house who can associate daily with their children and grandchildren and yet can be separate.

Although the practice of remaining on the farm is not based on economic considerations, it does have economic applications. The old people do not need many of the world's goods. Most of their food is grown right on the farm. There is no rent to pay and no house to buy and this means that the family assets are conserved in the community.[1]

---

[1] Walter M. Kollmorgan, *The Old Amish of Lancaster County, Pennsylvania, Rural Life Studies, U. S. Dept. Agric., Bur. Agric. Econ.,* No. 4, pp. 61-63.

How satisfying is the role of the aged in this picture of their life in the Amish community. They possess economic security. They retire gradually from agricultural and household activities. They apparently maintain just the right combination of separation from and association with the members of their families. They enjoy an assured status in the community.

How different is the lot of the unskilled worker in the city. Typically, by sixty-five he is out of a job and may have lost it some time before. He has no savings and does not own his home, or, if he does, it is probably mortgaged. He is eligible for old-age assistance, but may remain on the waiting list for some months before he receives the small monthly check. He and his wife drop the organizations in which they have been members because they are not able to pay dues. Their children are financially unable to give their parents much assistance. Often the relations of the parents with the children and grandchildren are strained or nominal. The old couple feel that they have no vital part in the life of the community.

Even today, the farmer and his wife who own their farm are able to make a relatively easy and simple adjustment to their declining physical powers and to the expectations of their children and of the community. The aging farmer gradually decreases his agricultural activities until he may be taking care only of his garden. His wife also diminishes her household tasks in accordance with reduced strength.

In the city, however, an increasing number of vocational activities are subject to compulsory retirement at the ages of seventy, sixty-five, and even sixty. The man who previously was employed eight or more hours a day may suddenly find himself unemployed and with nothing of importance to do to occupy his leisure time. In addition, then, to organic and psychological changes which accompany aging, the man over sixty is confronted with the perplexing question of adjustment to a changed social role.

The problem of personal adjustment in old age is all the

more difficult today because society has failed to redefine the functions of the older adult in the modern urban world. In all previous cultures — primitive, ancient, medieval — old persons had a recognized, and with few exceptions, the most important social role. In our own society the general tendency has been to discard the aged, to put them on the shelf, and at best to pension them or at worst to provide them with a pittance hardly enough under old-age assistance for physical subsistence — often not enough to keep body and soul together.

It is in the light of this transition from a rural to an urban civilization that the growing problems of aging are to be understood and studied. In fact, directly or indirectly, the problems of aging become accentuated and intensified to a great extent because of the shift from a rural scene, favorable to the aged, to an urban environment that is indifferent to the needs and claims of its older residents. In our further discussion of the increasing problems of the older persons, abrupt severance from a lifetime occupation, difficulty in finding satisfying and vital substitute activities, economic insecurity, loss of status, decreasing social participation in organizations, and greater unhappiness and maladjustment get meaning and significance in an urbanized society.[2]

A growing and most difficult problem for many, if not for most older adults, is the abrupt retirement from an occupation because of having reached a certain age. The profession, trade, or other work activity in which a person has engaged is a central part, the core, of his personality. From the day in childhood or youth when he chose his occupation, he has identified himself with it. It has been his chief role in life for which he prepared and through which he has performed his service to society. Yet at a given age he must make a sharp break with his past and seek if possible a substitute in some other activity. For-

[2] For other discussions of response to loss of work, see Chapters IV and V.

tunately, there are still certain occupational activities apart from farming where there is a transition from full to partial employment. For example, both the physician and the lawyer can reduce their practice, or the practice naturally falls off with aging. It would be of interest to make a study of sudden versus gradual retirement by comparing the adjustment and happiness of teachers who are forced to retire and of lawyers who gradually relinquish their practice.

It is much more difficult in the city than in the country to find satisfying and vital substitute activities for the discontinued occupational role. The farmer can take up gardening, a kindred activity. A superannuated city-dweller may, and often does, take up a hobby, and this, of course, is all to the good. The serious question, however, is whether the hobby has vital significance to the person. The hobby differs from work in an important characteristic. Both are interesting activities, but work has social value whereas a hobby is only of value to the individual. This is the reason a hobby is seldom a satisfactory substitute for an occupation. Incidentally, it is why recreational activities, however valuable in themselves, fail to take the place of work. To the extent, however, that either a hobby or a recreational activity does take on social value, then it becomes more significant.[3] Accordingly, hobby shows or hobbies that bring in money, or recreational activities that represent identification with a group and where winning has group reference, have social value and therefore greater significance to older people.

Urban life usually rewards youth and penalizes old age. Economic insecurity has been greatly increased in our industrial society, particularly for the man or woman unemployed in the fifties and the sixties. Our federal system of social security and old-age assistance is an attempt to meet this problem. At present the grants and the benefits are inadequate and are becoming increasingly so with the continued rise in the cost of living.[4]

[3] See Chapter VII for a discussion of hobbies and other leisure-time activities.
[4] Chapters IX and X consider the problem of financial security in some detail.

Older persons, as has already been pointed out, have much lower status in American than in other societies. This is in part due to their enforced retirement from occupational activity and to their greatly reduced income after sixty-five. But it is in large part the result of our over-evaluation of youth and our underevaluation of maturity. The sense of being discarded, of having no vital function, is the most significant aspect of this loss of status. The contrast is the sharpest in the case of a man at the height of his career and in a position of power and influence before retirement who finds that after retirement his voice carries little or no weight and his opinions are not sought.

With old age also comes decreasing participation in social organizations. This may be due to the contraction of activities which accompany declining physical vigor and diminishing social interests. In our studies of old people, however, we find an even more important factor is the lack of funds to pay dues, to maintain a respectable appearance, or to engage in entertaining. Giving up clubs and other organizational memberships is a real trial to the aging person and deprives him of a resource most important for his mental health and social well-being.

As might have been expected from the foregoing list of the growing problems of aging in our modern society there is the increasing unhappiness, unadjustment, and maladjustment of old people. In general, they are unhappier after sixty-five than they were before. Some of this unhappiness derives from causes that are unavoidable, such as loss of relatives and friends by death. Much of it can be reduced, as for example, that resulting from ill health. More unhappiness than we perhaps think can be eliminated or greatly diminished if economic security and opportunity for continued occupational activity and vital participation in community life can be provided. This conclusion is strengthened by the fact that persons who meet old age and its problems of adjustment successfully often state that this period is the happiest in their lives.

There remain certain other problems of aging that seem not to have increased, at least markedly, in the shift from the country to the city. Among these are bereavement caused by the death of a spouse, child, or close friend, loss of the companionship of friends because of the vicissitudes of life or diminishing physical vigor.[5] Yet each of these appears to be indirectly affected by the transition from the rural to the urban way of life. Bereavement seems more acute when the person lacks economic security and status and when he has no occupational or other vital interest activity. The loss of friends is felt more keenly for the same reason. A person is likely to become more concerned about his physical ailments if he is not occupied by other activities and interests.

From the examination of the evidence, the conclusion is inescapable that the problem of aging is growing in magnitude and in seriousness. In this field there is evident need of research as a basis for a national policy and to determine the type of services most helpful to older persons. In planning research it is important to be aware, first, that old age comprises four decades; second, that the needs and wishes of old people and their attitudes should be of central concern; third, that the transition to old age is a crucial period of personal adjustment; fourth, that instruments for the measurement of personal adjustment are important; fifth, that the attitude of the public and the value of old persons to society are significant factors in the situation.

OLD AGE NOT A UNITARY PERIOD

Old age spans the four decades of the sixties, the seventies, the eighties, and the nineties — as long a period of time as early and middle maturity combined. The number of persons in each succeeding decade is smaller than in the preceding years, but numbers are likely to grow as modern medicine and public health measures increase the life

[5] This problem is considered by Dr. Frohlich in Chapter V.

expectancy. Data from a pioneer study are available that provide information upon the differential characteristics of older people by five-year periods from sixty to ninety-nine years. These findings were obtained from 499 men and 759 women who filled out schedules in answer to questions about their activities and their attitudes.[6] The persons included in the study were all of the white race and were men and women who were older, more highly urbanized, better educated, and more representative of business and professions than is the general population. The percentages of persons in the study group and in the general population who were married and widowed were very similar as were also percentages of men without paid employment.

The trend with increasing age from the sixties through the nineties may be briefly summarized from the data as presented by Dr. Ruth S. Cavan. Increase in age is associated with:

A higher percentage of widows and widowers

A higher percentage living in dependent family relationships — in institutions, with sons or daughters, with relatives

A decrease in amount of close companionship

A decrease in participation through attendance at meetings, offices held, number of hobbies, and plans for the future

A decline in the gainful employment of males

Greater dependence on pensions, old-age assistance, and children for support

Increase in physical handicaps, illness, and nervousness, and a decrease in feeling of satisfaction with health

Increase in religious activities and in dependence upon religion

Decrease in feelings of happiness, usefulness, zest for living, and a corresponding increase of lack of interest in life

Lower median attitude score, indicating poorer adjustment.

 [6] Ruth S. Cavan, Robert J. Havighurst, Ernest W. Burgess, and Herbert Goldhamer, *Personal Adjustment in Old Age* (Chicago: Science Research Associates, 1949).

THE NEEDS AND WISHES OF OLD PEOPLE

It is easy to think of the problems of old people in terms of statistics. The magnitude of the problem, of course, must be known, but it is also important to perceive the problem in other than numerical terms. For an adequate understanding it is essential to consider older persons as human beings with needs, wishes, and aspirations.

The virtue of case studies in contrast with statistics is that they give the research worker access to the inner life of the person and to the subjective aspects of the problem. In research upon older people it is particularly important that we see their needs through their own eyes.

In the study *Personal Adjustment in Old Age* a limited number of life histories were secured. A reading of these makes feasible the formulation of the needs of older persons in relation to the theory of the fundamental wishes, as set forth by W. I. Thomas. These wishes are security, new experience, response, and recognition.

Security. The need of old persons for security is basic. It is manifested in four different ways. First, they desire good health, not only for its own sake but because it makes possible the strength and vitality to set about the fulfillment of their other needs. They seek economic security, again not so much for its own sake but because it is a means to the expression of other human aspirations. They want also emotional and mental security, "peace of mind," in the words of the late Dr. Liebman. As they age they turn increasingly to religion for certainty in the realm of spiritual things.

New experience. The desire for stimulating experiences is frequently frustrated in old age. Many accept the dictum of society that their day is done and make little or no effort to keep mentally alert and to continue participation in the events of the world about them. Too many old people lack the inner resources to find and to engage in stimulating activities.[7] Yet old as well as young people

[7] Dr. Donahue also discusses the need for purposeful activity. See Chapter IV.

have this basic need for new experience. This is indicated
by the many old persons who maintain a vigorous and often
a creative interest in life and who are animated by the
spirit of the aging Ulysses that "it is not too late to seek
a newer world."

Response. Older persons want affection and the expression of intimate appreciation. Yet they experience great
emotional crises in the death of their spouses and of their
closest friends. For women bereavement appears to be
the greatest trial, and for men retirement from work.
Widows remarry less frequently than do widowers, partly
because they are more emotionally bound up with the departed spouse, partly because of their greater longevity,
and, also, because widowers apparently prefer younger
mates for second wives. Younger and middle-aged adults
often lack sympathetic understanding of the needs for affection, and particularly for sex expression, of older adults.

Recognition. No matter what their age, people want to
perform a role in society that has a social function and that
gives recognition. The American public as we have seen
is indifferent to the functionless role of the aged. Instead,
it tends to be critical of those who cling tenaciously to
positions of power and influence.

Three principles of the fundamental wishes will help
to clarify the importance of this analysis of the needs of old
people. First of all, every person needs expression of all
four wishes for a wholesome life. Otherwise, if one or
more do not find expression he will be unadjusted and may
become maladjusted. Second is the principle of nonsub-
stitution, which means that an activity in the field of one
wish cannot be a satisfactory substitute for an activity in
the field of another wish. The third principle is that of
sublimation, or that, if an activity in one field is blocked,
it can be satisfied by an activity within the same field at the
same or higher social value.

This analysis, in terms of wishes, underscores the fact
that modern urban society is failing to meet the essential

needs of older persons. It emphasizes the point that the provision for old people at a subsistence level is not a sufficient answer to their human needs and aspirations.

PERSONAL AND SOCIAL ADJUSTMENT

At this place in the discussion it is clear why many old persons are not adjusted in our society. It is because our society is not adjusted to them. This point brings us to the consideration of the concepts of personal and social adjustment — how they differ from each other and how they are interrelated:

Personal adjustment to aging may be defined as the restructuring of attitudes and behavior to enable the person in response to a new situation to achieve the integrated expression of his wishes and aspirations in a form that also satisfies the expectations and demands of society. Personal adjustment finds its context in social adjustment. Social adjustment is the adaptation of society or one of its institutions to social change. It is the process of revising social standards and procedures in order to increase social efficiency and/or the personal adjustment of its members.[8]

Personal and social adjustment as these definitions imply are closely interrelated. The great problem of personal adjustment of old people, as we have seen, arises from the transition from a rural society in which they were well adjusted to an urban environment which provides little or no place for them. Real social adjustments are necessary to assure old persons a more favorable environment for the expression of their fundamental wishes and their social needs.

Changes in society take time. Until they are made, old persons must make their own personal adjustment to the existing situation. There exists a great field for the improvement of personal adjustment of old people to changing conditions in their lives.

An outline of the stages in the cycle of personal adjustment as applied to the crisis of aging may be helpful to those engaged in research or social service. Five stages

[8] Cavan, Havighurst, Burgess, and Goldhamer, *op. cit.*, p. 10.

may be differentiated. The first represents the challenge of adjustment and the second the initial response of the old person who is stimulated to success or is frustrated in his effort to solve the problem. The next stages are those of unadjustment, maladjustment, and readjustment. They are outlined with reference to the problems of adjustment in old age:

1. The first stage is the challenge of a new situation such as retirement from work or bereavement in the loss of a spouse.

2. The second stage is either that of stimulation to immediate adjustment or frustration. In case of adjustment the person puts forth successful efforts to master the problem. The retired teacher, for example, may engage in writing a textbook or turn to part-time work on a chicken ranch. In case of frustration, the older person is likely to manifest excessive activity, sometimes by way of trial and error, sometimes by alternations of excited and depressed behavior, or is finally driven to more careful analysis of the problem leading to its solution. When the wife loses a husband to whom she has been devoted she may give way to prolonged sorrow and grief. Finally, on advice of friends she may take renewed interest in life. She may find employment or assume an active role in a civic or welfare organization.

3. The third stage, if the person does not adjust in the second stage, is a period of unadjustment characterized by feelings of anxiety, despair, despondency, hopelessness, guilt, or remorse. The person may still make periodic frantic, desperate, or half-hearted attempts to adjust or he may abandon the effort. He may become restless and engage in random behavior.

4. The fourth stage is that of maladjustment where a nonadaptive activity is substituted for the desired one. This activity represents both social and mental maladjustment. Examples are eccentric behavior, alcoholism, phobias, invalidism, excessive gambling, psychoneuroses, and psychoses.

5. The fifth stage is that of readjustment which may follow upon either the third stage of unadjustment or the fourth stage of maladjustment. Readjustment may result from any one of the following:

a) Reorientation of attitude. Often the chief obstacle to adjustment to a changed or new situation is the attitude of the person which prevents his use of some appropriate activity. Frequently in old age the greatest difficulty in adjustment is the rigid attitude of nonacceptance of the situation. The retired person refuses to face the reality of the necessary adjustments to be made with reduced income. The patient with a cardiac condition does not comply with his physician's instructions. The widow, cherishing the memory of her husband, wears out her welcome with friends by her constant reminiscences and eulogies of him. In all these cases the chief requisite to satisfactory adjustment is a reorientation of attitudes.

b) Adaptation of activities. Almost all the readjustments in old age are in the nature of reduction of activities or of modifying them to meet declining physical vigor and/or reduced income. The physician limits his practice to fewer office hours. The retired Y.W.C.A. secretary teaches a Sunday School class of adolescent girls.

The majority of older persons find it relatively easy to reorient their attitudes and to readapt their activities. The minority of them experience more or less difficulty in making the desired change in attitude or in engaging in or learning a new activity. These may need help in making their adjustment.[9]

Three different kinds of resources are, or should be, available to help persons reorient their attitudes or adapt their attitudes to the problem of aging:

Friendly advice and professional services. The retired person may discuss his problems with his wife, with his closest friend, a lodge brother, his physician, or his pastor.

[9] The adjustment process is developed from the point of view of the psychologist in Chapter IV.

They may help him to make up his mind about his plans for the future. In mediating specific adjustments his physician may prescribe changes in diet and habits; and his pastor may help to comfort him in facing the death of a wife.

Provision for education in new activities. In old age the stress is upon adaptation of activities, but often the old person needs to learn some new activity. The retired businessman learns how to raise and care for chinchillas. His wife takes lessons in painting. Persons who never had time for hobbies pore over books and pamphlets containing instructions and information upon the subject.

The vast amount of unused leisure time of older persons is a challenge to adult education to investigate their needs and interests and to provide both a program for the learning of activities and skills and also one for general education in historical, cultural, and political fields.

The utilization of counseling and therapy. Persons with marked unadjustment or with a maladjustment seldom are able individually or with the assistance of friends to make readjustments. They need special and skilled assistance that may be beyond the competence of even their physician or minister. Nondirective counseling may be helpful, especially in cases of conflict over life values or confusion about one's goal in life. Frequently, the older person is in need of information about practical ways of acting in specific situations, which he can obtain from a counseling or service center for old people where available. In cases of extreme maladjustment, psychiatric diagnosis and treatment are necessary.

This statement of the cycle of the adjustment process places its phases in relation to each other in a way which should facilitate both research and service.

INSTRUMENTS FOR MEASURING AGING

It is important both for significant research in aging and for improved service to older persons to devise instruments of measurement. Three such instruments will be described with some indication of their value for research and for service. These instruments are measurements of social participation, attitudes, and aging. Instruments for the measurement of social participation and of attitudes have already been devised and are fully described in the monograph on *Personal Adjustment in Old Age*.[10] The designing of an index of aging is proposed as an important objective for further research.

The index of social participation. The index of social participation covers questions on nineteen items. Four questions on health are included, since health is an important factor conditioning activities. The health items are: the number of serious physical problems, the number of minor physical difficulties, days confined in bed in a year, and amount of care required. The activity items are as follows: use of leisure time, number of hobbies, extent of reading, number of organizations in which the person is active, number of club or other group meetings each month, frequency of listening to radio, attendance at religious services, frequency of reading Bible, frequency of seeing friends, frequency of seeing children and young people, frequency of seeing family or close relatives, frequency of spending holidays with them, with whom living, employment, and things given up because of reduced income.

The answers to these items are scored and range from three to forty-three on the experimental group of 102 persons on whom they were standardized. The schedule may be used cautiously with individuals as a quick way of getting an idea of their participation in activities and for purposes of comparison with others. In research it may be employed in making comparisons between groups, as, for example, if it is desired to find out the difference in social participation between old people residing in their own homes as compared with those living with children or other relatives.

[10] Cavan, Havighurst, Burgess, and Goldhamer, *op. cit.*

The attitude index. Even more important than participation in activities is the attitude of the person toward his participation or lack of participation. The attitude index as it is organized at present contains questions directed to secure attitudes relating to his health status, to his economic security, to his happiness, to his feelings of usefulness, and to six areas of activity, namely his family, friends, leisure, membership in organizations, work, and religion. There are seven statements in each area, ranging from a very low to a very high evaluation. The person is asked to check each of these statements as true or false. On the basis of the reports of attitudes a total score is secured which is taken as representing the degree of satisfaction or dissatisfaction of the person with his present status. The score on the attitude index was correlated with that on the index of social participation and yielded a Pearsonian r of $+ .78$. It was also correlated with a personal adjustment score derived from the ratings of a group of old persons by field workers in the study, which gave a Pearsonian r of $+ .74$.

Although neither of these correlations can be accepted as a conclusive test of the validity of the instrument, they serve to give confidence in it as a tentative measure until a superior instrument has been derived.

The attitude index may be used clinically as one way of ascertaining the personal adjustment of an individual, but should be checked by other data obtained from him and from others. It can be used in research when it is desired to check the attitudes of groups of persons as, for example, after a change of policy or/and program in an institution for aged persons.

Index of aging. At present chronological age is our only measure of aging. There is great need of an instrument that will provide in realistic terms an index of aging. Such an instrument should be designed to ascertain the actual process of aging in its physiological, psychological, and social aspects. For example, physiological aging would be concerned with organic conditions, such as heart trouble, psychological aging with decline of mental ability, and sociological aging with contraction of social activities and interests. The age of the person could be then expressed, not in terms of chronological years but in terms of physiological, psychological, and social age.[11]

The value of this index of aging is obvious. When it has been designed and standardized, retirement could be based on the scientific determination of the physiological, psychological, and social efficiency of the person rather than by the number of years he has lived. Part-time work might be assigned also with consideration of functional rather than of chronological age.

These three instruments for the measurement of social participation, attitudes toward life, and aging are, to repeat, valuable for research and for service to old people.

THE PUBLIC AND THE PROBLEM OF AGING

The present crisis of old age, as we have seen, derives very largely from conditions associated with the transition from a rural to an urban civilization. In an industrial society, with the emphasis upon speed, efficiency, and competition, the old are tossed upon the scrap pile.

The public has become concerned with the problem of the old but only in a superficial way and to a limited extent. Its attitude of indifference has changed to that of pity. Through social security and old-age assistance it has provided what is often not more than a pittance for the subsistence of its older citizens. The willingness of the public for the government to assume the support of the aged was, in all probability, partly due to the desire of relatives to be free of this responsibility.

Research is needed to secure the facts that will enlighten the public upon the nature of the problem of aging in relation to society. According to our hypothesis, these facts should demonstrate that the crux of the problem lies in the

[11] In Chapter III, Dr. Stieglitz discusses some of the difficulties involved in constructing an index of aging.

undefined and consequent uncertain status of old people in our society. Their status needs to be redefined in the light of the findings of research upon their capabilities and aspirations and the need of society for their services.

At present there exist puzzling anomalies in the role of the older persons in our society. Responsible leaders in the business world, in civic affairs, and in politics are men in their sixties and over. Herbert Hoover and Bernard Baruch are two of our elder statesmen whose advice has been repeatedly sought by our government in recent years. W. C. Lehman has published findings from a study which demonstrates that the average age of American political leaders has steadily increased since the founding of the republic.

It is evident also that older persons who are the first to be discharged when there is an abundance of labor are called back into service when there is a labor shortage. Recent studies indicate that older workers compensate for lack of speed by other characteristics, such as greater care and dependability. Evidently, more extensive and intensive studies should be made of the relative efficiency and productivity of older and younger workers.

Then, too, there is growing evidence that the country needs the productivity of older workers to ensure national prosperity. At present about 60 per cent of the population are between twenty and sixty-five years of age and 7½ per cent are sixty-five and older. In 1990 the proportion of persons between twenty and sixty-five will remain practically the same, but the proportion sixty-five and over will be almost twice as large as it is at the present time. If these old people are to be fully or partly supported, an increasingly heavy burden will be placed upon young and middle-aged adults.

Prosperity for all demands increased productivity. To the extent of their competence old people should be encouraged to continue in full-time and in part-time work. Otherwise, the nation is wasting its human resources.

Research should also be directed to the discovery of

ways of utilizing the services of older persons in activities which have social value although they bring no financial compensation. One enlightening study for this purpose would record successful, satisfying careers of retired persons.

Findings from research are essential if the public is to understand the real nature of the problem of aging, to redefine the role of older people in our society, and to restore to them a significant social function.

Research on aging in its biological and psychological aspects is more developed than in its social phases. Fortunately, a research planning memorandum on social adjustment in old age is being published by the Social Science Research Council.[12] This memorandum outlines the present stage of research on the economic and social aspects of aging and suggests significant projects for further research.

SUMMARY

In conclusion, the chief points presented by this paper may be briefly summarized. The problem of aging is increasing in importance not only because of the larger percentage of people in the period of later maturity but because their role and function in society has been greatly disturbed and lowered by the transition from a rural to an urban economy. Their place in modern society needs to be redefined. For that purpose a program of research on aging, particularly in its social aspects, is necessary. Such research needs to take into account the four decades which comprise old age, the needs and wishes of older persons, their problems of personal adjustments, the instruments necessary for measuring their adjustment, and, finally, the public attitude to the problem, particularly with reference to the potential economic and social value of older people. Our older citizens are a valuable human resource which is now being wasted. We need research to determine how they may be best utilized and conserved.

[12] Otto Pollak, *Social Adjustment in Old Age* (New York: Social Science Research Council, 1948).

II
Biologic Aspects of the Aging Process

By Carl V. Weller

Carl V. Weller, M.S., M.D., is professor of pathology and chairman of the Department of Pathology at the University of Michigan. He is a member of the National Research Council, the American Association for Cancer Research, and former president of the American Association of Pathologists and Bacteriologists. He is co-author of Medical Aspects of Mustard Gas Poisoning *and author of the "Hemolymph Node," a chapter in the* Handbook of Hematology. *He is past editor of* Contributions to Medical Science, Annals of International Medicine, *and present editor of the* American Journal of Pathology.

WE GROW OLD NATURALLY

WE GROW old naturally. That is a statement which has no unpleasant connotation. It is a simple statement of a truth, the appreciation of which is essential if the process of aging is to be understood, accepted, and utilized for the benefit of man. If the order of the words is changed to "naturally, we grow old," the implication becomes less pleasant. Far different concepts of old age are entertained by the child, the young adult, the middle-aged, and those in late middle life. Those who say "naturally, we grow old" speak without complete understanding. They do not realize that they were growing old before they were born. I propose to show that the process of growing old is as normal and as natural as life itself.

That man grows old naturally is evident from the pattern of life. Man is one of the long-lived animals. Despite popular belief to the contrary, only giant tortoises[1] have a longer life span. Sixty years is the longest authenticated life for an elephant and fifty-four years for a parrot, both of them belonging to species to which great longevity is popularly attributed. A dog at fourteen years is said to be as old as

[1] F. Thone, *Science News Letter,* January 24, 1948.

a man of eighty, and our familiar laboratory white rats are senile at four years. Thus, for each species there is an ultimate life limit which not all members of the species reach. Within the life span of the individuals of each species a pattern of life has been established which, through a long period of trial, has proved most successful for the perpetuation of that species. We cannot escape that pattern. It is indelibly stamped into the living nuclear substance which determines heredity. That the pattern is different for each species is evidence enough that it can be modified, but alteration of the life pattern is an unbelievably slow process. For man, change in the life pattern and therefore in the ultimate life limit, if it is occurring at all, is at too slow a rate to be recognized in the lifetime of any observer. It is doubtful if there has been any clearly recognizable change in the human pattern in the few thousand of years which comprise the historical record of our species.

For each species of animal or plant the established life pattern is wholly an expression of the biological mechanisms for securing perpetuation of the species. That purpose is never out of sight. Consequently, the pattern can always be interpreted as purposeful. It makes not a particle of difference to my thesis, or to the wholesome appreciation of the aging process which I hope to impart to you, whether you write "nature" with an initial capital and think of God, the Creator, as the directing force in human life; or whether you think of nature in terms of evolution and involution, and of the life pattern as the result of processes of trial and error extending through ranges of time known only to the geologist and the astronomer. Whichever, or whatever, your personal philosophy may be, it is equally applicable to a genuine understanding of why and how we grow old naturally.

The impelling, dynamic drive to secure the continuity of the species determines the pattern of life, but the factors concerned are numerous, and the duration and intensity of the instinctive urge for procreation is but one of them.

Another is the length of the period of gestation during which the developing infant remains unborn. For man, this is about ten lunar months. Still other factors are the number of young born at one time, their degree of development at birth, the length of the period of physical growth, the age at which procreation becomes possible, the length of the training period for the acquisition of knowledge and skills, the extent of the period of fertility, and the duration of the need for parental (particularly, maternal) care before the succeeding generation can, in turn, assume an independent role in the pattern of life. Innumerable examples of the varying devices by which nature makes adjustments for these biological needs can be found. The adult guinea pig and the adult rat are of approximately the same size. For the guinea pig the period of gestation is about sixty-three days and the average litter is between two and three young. For the rat, the period of gestation is about twenty days and the average litter is about nine. But note the compensatory factors for these marked differences! The newborn guinea pig has its eyes open, it weighs about eighty grams, it is capable of active locomotion, and it takes some food other than its mother's milk. The newborn rat is a tiny, hairless, blind infant, capable of wriggling motion only, and entirely dependent upon the maternal food supply for many days. Each pattern is successful in maintaining the species. "Pigs Is Pigs" caught the popular fancy a generation or so ago; and the brown rat is an almost worldwide pest, although the ingenuity of man is constantly pitted against him.

Applied to man, intra-uterine life extends for about 280 days, fully dependent infancy lasts about two years, and partly dependent childhood for another decade or more. Physiologically, reproduction usually becomes possible at twelve to seventeen years of age, but our highly technical culture requires a longer period for the acquisition of knowledge and skill. After the training period, there is a further interval before economic independence is assured.

Thus, parenthood is usually delayed until the middle of the third decade. Since maternal care is desirable for fifteen years or more after a child is born, the reason for the cessation of female fertility at about forty-five years of age at once becomes evident. The normal life expectancy must provide for maternal care after the birth of the last child. The paternal part in bringing the infant to the stage of independent living is far less intimate, as we all realize. We are not surprised, therefore, to find that there is no fixed limit upon male fertility. Many men of advanced years retain the possibility of fatherhood.

There is still another phase of the life pattern, both for the lower animals and for man. In securing the perpetuation of the species, nature must utilize the individual, but when the end has been served the individual is no longer needed. To be sure, those of advanced years may be of value to the tribe because they can impart their knowledge and skill to the young hunters and warriors. The maturity of judgment gained by experience makes the aged of use as counselors. Their main task has been accomplished, however, and soon they are to be removed from the scene. The tempo of the aging process increases, the initial energy charge is finally expended, and death may be physiologic if disease does not intervene.

From this rapid survey of the biologic pattern of life it should be recognized that the entire process is natural, it is purposeful, and it is for the good of our species. The aging process is a part of the master scheme of life. The process of aging is racially altruistic!

How natural it is to grow old becomes evident at once with the not unpleasant discovery that we commence growing old before we are born. Nature is economical. Useless structures undergo atrophy and disappear, or are otherwise disposed of. Those who have some familiarity with embryology will recall that in the development of the human egg cell, the ovum, three-fourths of the nuclear material is discarded. The tail of the spermatozoon is absorbed after the spermatozoon has entered the ovum. The placental blood vessels show senile changes at the time of birth. Throughout the entire development period these involuntary processes take place. The roots of the milk teeth are absorbed and the thymus gland and the tonsils diminish in size. These and many other alterations are part of the process of growing old, even in childhood and adolescence.

After adult stature has been attained the aging process continues. It influences the character of the diseases of middle life and of old age, but we are not now discussing individual diseases. There are recognizable tissue changes which become more and more evident as the years advance. Reasonably enough, these are of the same character as those found in the mature (senile) placenta which was discarded when the person was born. These are the basic changes in physiologic involution.[2] They fall into three groups:

1. Reduction in size of organs and of the organism as a whole. This is physiologic atrophy and is brought about in part by reduction in number of cells and in part by reduction in size of cells. Replacement and repair, effective in earlier years, have become inadequate to offset the attrition of use.

2. Changes in the intercellular and supporting tissues of the body which increase the proportion of connective tissues as compared to the more actively functioning elements. These same supporting tissue elements become less cellular and more dense and hyaline. Elasticity is diminished, and there is a strong tendency toward the deposition of calcium and magnesium salts — calcification.

3. Alterations in the blood vessels characterize the aging process more than any other general feature. Normally, arteries have elastic walls which expand as the pulse wave comes along and contract upon the contained blood after it passes. These large elastic vessels serve to equalize and control blood pressure in much the same way that the air

[2] These are discussed also in Chapter III in connection with maintenance of health.

compression chamber of a force pump gives a steady stream from the nozzle. In the aging process and as a part of the major involution which is to remove the unneeded organism from the scene, blood vessels lose much of their elasticity; their walls become thicker; muscle and elastic fibers are replaced by nonelastic hyaline substance; lime salts are laid down in the wall; and the lumen, through which the blood flows, becomes progressively more narrow.

These changes in the blood vessels constitute the process of vascular sclerosis, popularly known as hardening of the arteries. Similar, if not identical, changes occur in certain blood vessels of babies, which must be obliterated in making over the fetal circulation into the postnatal pattern. No one thinks of these infantile adjustments as disease. There is no more reason for thinking of the vascular changes of late middle life and old age as disease. Yet they exact certain penalties from the human body, and many of the ailments which are considered as more or less peculiar to advanced years are the functional expression of impaired blood supply to important organs as a result of these same, apparently physiologic, vascular changes. The results are noted particularly in the musculature of the heart, in the kidneys, and in the brain. While these retrogressive changes in the blood vessels appear to be as natural and as inevitable for the involutionary period as growth is for the earlier decades of life, it is not too much to hope that medical science may discover more effective methods than are now available for postponing their onset or retarding their development. But this is a difficult task, since it means modifying processes which are a part of the hereditary pattern of life itself.

Just as life and the aging process, which is a part of life, exhibit a pattern which is peculiar to the species, so, also, do the functional components of human activity. They show varying phases of emphasis in respect to age that are most desirable in securing the perpetuation of the species. In Figure 1 the curves for nutrition and metabolism, motility, reproductive power in the female, and cerebral and spiritual development have been drawn in relation to the decades of life. The ascent and decline of these vital functions reflect biologic needs, the satisfaction of these needs, and the effects of involutionary changes. The function of nutrition and metabolism is at its highest pitch at birth, declines rapidly until about twenty years of age, remains at a nearly constant level until about seventy, and then gradually falls again until the end of life. We are better machines for taking in food, building bodies, and producing energy at

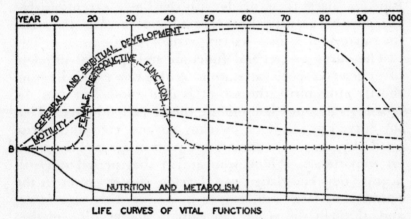

LIFE CURVES OF VITAL FUNCTIONS

Fig. 1. The curves of proportionate activity of four vital functions in the successive decades of life. (After Stratz and Warthin, with modifications.)

birth than we will ever be again. The function of motility, having in mind both the magnitude and velocity of motion and also motor skill, is exhibited at a low level at birth and rises rapidly after infancy to reach a broadly rounded summit in the third decade. Athletes and coaches know that at a period varying from about twenty-five to thirty years motor skill and the precise control of motor activity begin to decline. This decline continues to advanced years. The curve of reproductive function, as the biologic requirements lead us to anticipate, rises abruptly at puberty from the zero level of birth to reach its acme at about twenty-six years of age, with a return to the zero line (for the female) at the average menopausal age of forty-five. In a monogamous social arrangement the reproductive function is thus concentrated in a period of about two or two and one-half decades. For reasons which I have already stated, this is as it should be for the good of the species, and it is purposeful and not accidental. We should not have children until we are physically and spiritually ready to care for them, and children should not be born so late in parental life that there is no normal prospect of parental care continuing until they become independent. The curve of reproductive function meets these needs with the single exception that the physical capacity for reproduction develops too early for our complex and exacting economy.

The curve of cerebral function and spiritual development deserves special attention. With a very rapid rise from shortly after birth, the ascent is continuous but at a decreasing rate until late middle life or early old age. That the curve can and does, in many persons, continue to rise until fifty, sixty, or even sixty-five years of age is of the greatest importance. Those who are in that period can still acquire new knowledge, can develop greater power in the synthesis of facts, can temper judgment with experience, and, through the years, can gain in appreciation of that which is good and beautiful and in the understanding of spiritual values. Contemplation of the four curves of major vital functions leaves no doubt wherein lie the possibilities for gracious living on the part of those who are in the later years of life.

WE, THE AGING, ARE BECOMING MORE IMPORTANT IN THE SOCIAL ORDER

That part of our population which is sixty-five years of age and older is constantly becoming more numerous, both actually and proportionately. In 1900, only 4.1 per cent of the population was sixty-five years of age or older;[3] by 1940 the proportion had increased to 6.8 per cent. It is

[3] Metropolitan Life Insurance Company, *Statistical Bull.*, 29, No. 4 (1948).

estimated that by 1960, 9 per cent, and by the end of the century 13 per cent, of the people in the United States will be in the old-age group. In actual numbers, in 1900 there were about three million people in the United States who were sixty-five or over; by 1940 this group numbered about nine million. It is estimated that there will be fourteen million in that bracket by 1960, and twenty-one and one-half million by the end of the century.[4] This changing distribution of our population in respect to age is not only the most important feature of modern demography, but it is also of the utmost significance in determining the social and economic pattern of our times. The "oldsters" are coming into their own.

As with all similar statistical analyses, there is a reciprocal relationship, percentage-wise, between the various component groups of any population. Thus, while 9.4 per cent of the inhabitants of the United States were under five years of age in 1945, it is estimated that this group will be but 6.8 per cent by 1975, even though the total number of these young children will be considerably greater than it is now.

Back of the changing age distribution of our population is, of course, the increase in the average duration of life. This is expressed as "life expectancy at birth." This is the average age which an infant, born at the time under consideration, will attain. It is an expression of longevity. There is indirect evidence that life expectancy in Greece, Rome, and Egypt of two thousand years ago was somewhat between twenty and thirty years.[5] In 1900 it was 49.2 years in the United States; in 1945 it was sixty-five years. This is a gain of 16.6 years within the memory of those now in middle life — a dividend of added years in the prime of life and in later maturity for the baby born in 1945. Note that the gain of the past forty-five years is almost as great as that achieved in the preceding 1900 years. This progress continues. Today, in 1948, it is probable that the expectation of life for a white male infant is about sixty-seven years.

[4] Changes in the composition of the population are discussed in Chapter I.
[5] Metropolitan Life Insurance Company, *Statistical Bull.*, 28, No. 10 (1947).

It is also proper to speak of life expectancy as of any particular age after birth. This is more interesting and more significant for those of us who are in that broad period generously referred to as late middle life. Today, the white male of fifty years has 732 chances per 1,000 of reaching age sixty-five; in 1900, he had 685 chances per 1,000 of reaching that age. For the white female of fifty years, there were 827 chances per 1,000 in 1945, as compared with 718 chances per 1,000 in 1900, of reaching age sixty-five. The prospect for living beyond age sixty-five has also improved in our own time. The expectation of life at age sixty-five is greater now than in 1900-1902 by one year for males, and by two years for females. As of today the white male of sixty-five years can expect to live twelve and one-half years longer on the average; the white female, fourteen and one-fourth years longer.[6]

It must be understood that increasing the life expectancy and changing the ultimate life limit of the species are far different matters. The ultimate life limit is the average time that the members of the species would live if they died from normal physiologic involution and without disease. For man, the ultimate life limit is probably about ninety years, with considerable individual variation. Life expectancy takes into account pathologic death, the result of disease, as well as the less common physiologic death by which nature removes the aged when life's course is fully run.

Two relationships between life expectancy and the ultimate life limit of the species must be pointed out. The first is that the achievements of the health sciences are lessening the gap between the two. Life expectancy at birth is already very close to the biblical threescore years and ten. Under ideal conditions, with all disease eliminated, the gap would disappear entirely. In other words, the medical sciences are endeavoring to assure each human being at birth the right to live to the ultimate biologic limit of his

[6] Metropolitan Life Insurance Company, *Statistical Bull.*, 29, No. 2 (1948).

species. Naturally, this ideal may be approached but it will not be reached. I have already pointed out that no sharp line can be drawn between conditions which are designated as degenerative diseases and the physiologic involution of old age. This is particularly true in respect to alterations in the blood vessels. Is arteriosclerosis at age eighty a disease or part of the normal involutionary aging of the organism?

The second consideration of importance is that the ultimate life limit will not be extended by the efforts of the health sciences. It is an inherent part of the life pattern of the species. Actually, there is some slender evidence that the ultimate life limit is being lowered to a slight degree. This evidence cannot be elaborated here, but the result probably depends upon the fact that life saving in infancy, childhood, and early maturity results in carrying certain biologically inferior persons along into late middle life, who, under a more rigorous regime or with less scientific aid, would have perished at an earlier age. Their less well-endowed protoplasm "runs down" physiologically at an earlier period than that of a sturdier group selected by adversity at an early age. At any rate, there is no scientific basis for the dreams of self-styled life extension experts who hold out hope that man will have an ultimate life limit of 125 to 150 years.

The gain in life expectancy is due to the successes of the health sciences in the prevention, diagnosis, and treatment of disease. Only illustrative examples can be mentioned. Babies with developmental disturbances, even of the heart, are saved by surgical procedures. Diphtheria is entirely subject to control and fatalities are very few. Typhoid fever has become all but unknown in this part of the world. Only the careless or the fanatical have smallpox. The infantile fatalities of the dreaded "second summer" are no more. For diabetes and pernicious anemia the means are available for preserving life at a level of economic independence. In the last few years numerous new drugs have been given the world which are more potent and more specific in the control of infections than anything previously known. By these, the mortality from pneumonia and from various other infectious diseases has been sharply reduced. Tuberculosis we still have with us, but the decline in both illness and death from this scourge has displaced it from its first place among the causes of death in 1900 to the seventh place which it now occupies.

From these scattered examples it will be seen that the salvage of life through the prevention and cure of disease has been especially operative in infancy, childhood, and early maturity. Since there has been no positive effect upon the ultimate life limit of the species, since physical immortality has not been, and never will be, provided for us by technologic progress, there is an inevitable reciprocal effect upon those diseases which are usually found in advanced years. One who has escaped infantile diarrhea lives on to add to the mortality from heart disease sixty-five years later; another, who was adequately protected against diphtheria, succumbs to apoplexy at a ripe old age; and many who would have been among the 195 per 100,000 per annum who died from tuberculosis in 1900, now escape tuberculosis only to contribute to the rising total of deaths from cancer. It has always been true that, when medicine is winning the battle in one salient, statistical analysis seems to indicate that it is being lost in another. Seldom is thought given to the far greater numbers exposed to the diseases of late middle life and old age. In this group, also, much is being done to prevent and cure disease.

Obviously, the changing age distribution of our population is having an important effect upon the practice of medicine. The metabolic and degenerative diseases of later life and the malignant neoplasms of middle life and old age are proportionately much more important. Out of this necessity, a new medical specialty has developed, that of geriatrics. While gerontology is the science dealing with old age and the aging process in all of its aspects, geriatrics is its medical branch. Geriatrics is for the aging what pediatrics is for childhood. It will prove to be an equally important division of medicine. Further proof that "oldsters" are of increasing importance.

THE AGING ARE STILL BIOLOGICALLY USEFUL

It is true that growing old is a natural process, the purpose of which is ultimately to remove those whose major usefulness to the species has come to an end. But usefulness to the species includes much more than the creation of children and rearing them to an age at which they are physically competent to make their own contribution to the endless stream of life. If it were not so, we would count each generation as fifteen or twenty years instead of a third of a century as is true for all practical purposes today. Even with primitive man, whose food needed only to be gathered and not to be produced, those of advancing years were of value to the community as demonstrators of how the procurement of food could best be achieved, and as counselors whose past experience made it possible for them to interpret the significance of changing seasons and of other features of a constantly varying environment.

It is still more true today than it was one hundred thousand years ago that the aging have further biologic usefulness after childbearing has been completed. The present social and economic pattern calls for the extension of parental care for many years after offspring have passed the pubertal period. Education is prolonged, skills must be acquired, shelter must be found, economic independence must be reasonably secure. For such reasons marriage and childbearing are delayed and offspring come late. Longer years of parental aid and counsel are needed. Or, if the second generation marries before independence is assured, grandparents become useful in assuming responsibilities for care and maintenance to a degree which may be somewhat at variance with the general pattern of life but leaves no doubt in the grandparental minds that their biologic duty is not yet ended.

It is particularly in those activities which depend upon maturity of cerebral function, memory of accumulated experiences, and increased skill, tact, and forbearance in human relations that the aging retain and augment their usefulness. They function as counselors and guides, and as the determiners of policy. With child-rearing completed, time and strength remain for an active share in civic affairs, in politics, in the church, or in the fraternal order. For some time the totality of cerebral function increases, and the opportunity for its use is at hand.[7]

THE CHIEF INGREDIENT IN THE PRESCRIPTION
FOR GROWING OLD HAPPILY

The first and the most important ingredient in the prescription for growing old graciously and happily is understanding — understanding of the naturalness of the process of growing old. This inevitable involution, which begins even before we are born, is but the fulfillment of biologic destiny. In growing old we are equally a part of the patterned life of the species as when we are rearing children. With this view accepted, the mind is left free to make the most of the declining years.

Those who are familiar with the lectures and books[8] of Aldred Scott Warthin, whose professorship in pathology in the University of Michigan was terminated by death in 1931, will realize to what an extent I have made this philosophy of life and of growing old my own in the preceding pages. In the preface to *Old Age* he defined his purpose in the following words:

... the presentation of a rational workable philosophy of Old Age as an antidote to the modern futilities of life-extension of the individual to extreme limits and of possible rejuvenation. The human race has advanced several points in both knowledge and philosophy since the time of Ponce de Leon. Today the scientific mind may

[7] For a similar view, see Chapter IV on psychological aspects of aging.

[8] A. S. Warthin, *Old Age, the Major Involution* and *The Creed of a Biologist, a Biologic Philosophy of Life* (New York: Paul B. Hoeber, 1930).

obtain satisfaction and happiness in the contemplation of the potentialities of the mortal individual in carrying-on and advancing the immortal potentiality of the germ plasm. On such a foundation there may be built a satisfying working philosophy of life.

I have had a similar purpose. Knowledge of the biologic significance of the aging process makes possible the acceptance of its manifestations with understanding. With this foundation laid, it is possible to avoid or, at least, to mitigate, many of the annoyances and inconveniences of the later years of life. At the same time it is possible to augment the satisfactions of that period — to capitalize, as it were, the special assets of later maturity. Practical advice on how this can be done will be found in the contributions of others who have made special study of the technics of growing old graciously.

With understanding, we, the aging, can agree with Cicero in *De senectute:* "Whatever is natural must be accounted good."

III

The Personal Challenge of Aging: Biological Changes and Maintenance of Health

By Edward J. Stieglitz

Edward J. Stieglitz, M.S., M.D., F.A.C.P., is a physician and gerontologist in Washington, D. C. He is associated with the Washington School of Psychiatry, is attending internist in Geriatrics at Chestnut Lodge Sanatorium, Rockville, Maryland, and is a member of the publication committee of the Journal of Gerontology. *He edited the book,* Geriatric Medicine, *and is the author of many articles and books, including* The Second Forty Years, Arterial Hypertension, *and* A Future for Preventive Medicine.

THE PROBLEM of aging is so immense that I should like to take a few moments for orientation. In order to comprehend any complicated situation involving human affairs or involving natural affairs in which human beings are not concerned, such as floods, wars, volcanoes, divorce, marriage, aging, and other potential catastrophies, we need to look at it from three perspectives. If we look at it only from one or two of these perspectives, we assume a very asymmetric viewpoint. The three perspectives can be easily defined by using magnification as our basic simile. First, we must examine the problem with the naked eye. The individual is indivisible; body and mind are one. The individual is the unit. Second, with a microscope, we can take this person apart with blood counts, kidney function tests, blood pressure observations, basal metabolism determinations, and various other procedures. When we study the individual microscopically and dissect him into his biological components, the cell becomes the unit of thought, rather than the individual. Lastly, we must stand back far enough so that we may look at this individual with a telescope and see him in relation to the total environment, social and physical, economic, biological, and historical.

The science of aging, or gerontology, includes all three of these facets or perspectives. Man is the core. Our motivation for study is concern with ourselves. I think we must start out with the basic premise that man as an individual, or as a species, is 100 per cent selfish in his motivations. The most generous individual is generous because it gives him satisfaction, and he is truly no more generous than the miser who gets his satisfaction in a different fashion. I know there are a great many people who resent this concept. Just because they resent it does not nullify its truth. As man is the core, the essential motivation for all our study, the direct personal or clinical application of knowledge concerning aging is one division of the science. This is geriatric medicine, in which the individual is the unit of thought.

The second division of gerontology is concerned with the biology of senescence. Here the cell is the unit of thought. Each of us is composed of approximately two billion cells. The world population, in contrast, consists of about two billion people. The third division of gerontology is concerned with the sociologic problems of the aging in this crowded world. The magnitude, complexity, and urgency of the sociologic problems of an aging population were presented here by Professor Burgess.[1] My assignment was to present to you some of the basic concepts of what aging is and what aging does to the individual. Despite the temptations toward digressions, I shall try to adhere to these two areas of the whole.

AGING DEFINED AND DESCRIBED

Aging may be defined as the element of time in living. Aging is part of living. Aging begins with conception and terminates with death. It cannot be arrested unless we arrest life. There is no elixir of eternal youth, thank good-

[1] See Chapter I.

ness! It would be dreadful to remain infants all our lives. We may retard aging or accelerate it, but we cannot arrest it while life goes on, because it is essentially an element of living. Living is a continuous process, variable in its rates. Aging slows as we grow older. This is one of the compensations for later years. Aging change is rapid in youth and even more rapid prenatally in the period between conception and birth.

Aging involves two simultaneous processes which operate continuously in spite of the fact that they are contradictory to one another. On the one hand growth or evolution occurs, on the other atrophy (which means shrinkage) or involution.[2] These processes continue throughout life, though at varying rates. We can observe illustrations of atrophy even before the infant is born in the disappearance of the gill clefts which first develop and then atrophy in the early mammalian embryo. At the time of birth, when the child begins to breathe and get its oxygen from the lungs instead of from the mother's circulation, the atrophy of certain arterial structures is indistinguishable under the microscope from the involutionary changes which we see late in life. The atrophic process is the same in the newborn infant and in the senile grandparent. A very interesting phenomenon occurs in the placenta or afterbirth. It becomes atrophic or "old" when its functional life is near termination. At nine months of pregnancy, there exists an intimate proximity and interdependence in a very young baby, a middle-aged mother, and a senile placenta. Biologically adjacent and functioning together are three widely divergent biological ages. Here is an area of study which has by no means been explored adequately.

On the other hand, growth continues late in life. The hair continues to grow throughout life, and certain hairs grow more vigorously than ever. The eyebrows become shaggy, and often about the ears there is a growth of bristly hairs that were not there in middle age and youth. The

2 See Chapter II by Dr. Weller for another discussion of this topic.

whiskers become heavier, more brittle, and thicker. The
lower jaw continues to grow throughout life, according to
reports of several anthropologists. These students of anat-
omy, however, do not tell whether the rate of this growth
in later years varies with the amount of wagging that the
lower jaw has done during the lifetime. It is quite possible
that such functional activity is a modifying factor, as we
shall see later. I am not being facetious.

Cells are the ultimate units of life. What can we learn
about the aging of cells? Here the biologist in search of
information is blocked, because individual cells do not age.
They grow to maturity, and then divide to create two young
daughter cells. Individual cells simply do not age in the
sense that an individual ages. With the exception of a very
few cells in our central nervous system, the brain, and spinal
cord, none of the cells of our bodies is as old as we are.
They are being replaced constantly with young cells. You
and I are constantly rubbing off our hides and developing
new skin underneath. The same process, without the fric-
tion, occurs in all other structures. So we come up against
an insurmountable difficulty in studying the aging of the
individual cell, because the individual cell does not age.

The classical, epoch-making studies of Carrel and his
associates with tissue cultures reveal precisely the same thing
as we have just deduced from general biology. Carrel started
growing a bit of chick embryo heart in a flask containing
a nutrient medium in 1912. In 1946, thirty-four years later,
descendants of these same cells were growing just as rapidly,
just as vigorously, utterly unchanged in their appearance
and characteristics, as the original culture started thirty-four
years previously. This period is several times the known
maximum life span of a chicken. Carrel concluded that
cells themselves were essentially immortal when given an
appropriate environment.

The limiting proviso is a fundamental clue to the mechanism of aging. Continuation of a culture of cells is possible
only if the culture medium in which it grows is sterile and

refreshed every forty-eight hours. If the medium is permitted to become depleted of necessary food elements and allowed to accumulate the toxic garbage of the living, growing cells, the tissue culture quickly degenerates and dies. The essence of senescence lies not in the cellular structure, but in the matrix fluid in which they live. This intercellular medium is often spoken of as the internal environment.

Perhaps some of you do not realize that we live in two environments — an external environment of social strife, stale air, tobacco smoke, grime, grit, wind, snow, competition, sunshine, love, and hate, and an internal environment which is extraordinarily stable. The internal environment varies very little chemically and very little physically. We are by no means healthy if our temperature varies more than a degree, or more than 1 per cent of the optimum. If the concentration of sugar in the blood rises above a certain level we are no longer biologically healthy. Or if the glucose content of the blood falls below a certain level we become ill. The same applies to the many other chemical elements included in the composition of the organism. There are many elaborate mechanisms for maintaining the constancy of this internal environment. If this internal environment is not maintained within a relatively narrow range, health is impaired. We may say that an optimum internal environment is synonymous with health; that an internal environment deviating from the desirable in some respects but still within tolerable limits, is equivalent to disease, but that any intolerable deviation of the internal environment leads to death. The constants, and by that I mean such factors as body temperature, pulse, blood pressure, chemical concentrations, and many other things which are relatively constant, are not actually changed by aging. These things are not absolutely constant, but vary within narrow limits. Normal body temperature is the same at eighty as it is at eight. Pulse rate varies relatively little with age under comparable conditions of rest. Of course, the child of eight is much more active and energetic than the individual of eighty, and thus reveals a more rapid pulse when active, partly because he is more active.

The concentration of sugar in the blood is the same at eight or eighty. Though there is no appreciable change in these constants, the ability to maintain equilibrium depreciates with aging. There is great diminution in tolerance for extremes. Older individuals cannot tolerate extremes of temperature. They become ill when they are cold. An annual trip to Florida and the desire to seek warmth in winter is an admission of senility.

Similarly, the elderly do not tolerate hot weather. Each summer in the twenty-five years of practice, I have seen anywhere from one to ten persons over seventy years of age collapse during a spell of hot weather. They seem to go all to pieces. Last week I saw a gentleman of eighty-four who, after several hot days, suddenly became too weak one morning to raise his head from his pillow. He has no recollection of a period of twenty-four hours. His collapse occurred because he did not compensate for the changed external environment by necessary dietary adjustments. All he needed was some salt. Two liters of saline solution were given into his vein, and in a few hours he wanted to get up and go home. You see, as we grow older we live by habit. He had not changed his habits. The hot weather made him sweat (in Washington we not only perspire, we sweat). Sweat is salty, but he drank only pure water and did not adjust to that necessity for an increased salt intake. His collapse was due purely to salt deficiency. Habit was the major cause of his difficulty. A child, whose dietary habits are not fixed by time, will usually demand salty food in hot weather. The older person responds to habit rather than makes adjustment to the environment.

The older person is less tolerant to starvation and to overeating. The ability to maintain a normal blood sugar concentration is lessened. Thus, it is frequently desirable for the aged to eat small quantities often, rather than to attempt to eat large amounts at longer intervals.

In the aged where the reaction to any stress is lessened, symptoms are less conspicuous. The symptoms of illness are not due to injury; they are due to the reactions of the body to the injury and in later life these reactions are less violent. We may see a man of seventy walking around, admitting he does not feel very well, but not complaining very much, despite the fact he is suffering from an extensive lobar pneumonia. Youngsters, like you people here, would be sick in bed. The older person's symptoms are much less conspicuous. Perhaps it is a blessing that illness in later years is associated with less subjective distress, but it is also a curse, inasmuch as medical attention is postponed. Too often the institution of therapy is delayed until such time that only a miracle can be expected to accomplish a cure. Pain is our friend, more precious than that dearest chum who warns us about halitosis. There are fewer accidents where there are stoplights.

RATE OF AGING

The rate of aging change is by no means fixed; it is extremely variable. Aging varies among different species. For example, a three-hundred-day-old rat (I mean the kind with hair all over and a long tail) has approximately the same biological age as a thirty-year-old man; a six hundred-day-old rat is the approximate biologic age of a sixty-year-old man. Such contrasting rates of living are readily comprehended. But even in the same species, as for example man, there is great variation in the rate of aging in different individuals and in different parts of the same individual at different times of the life span.

Dr. Burgess said this morning that he hoped that ultimately there would be developed an index to the true age of an individual.[3] It will be extremely difficult to develop such an index. It will not be simple, because none of us is of the same biologic or physiologic age throughout. Different structures have different biologic ages. As I men-

[3] Dr. Burgess discusses the need for such an index in Chapter I.

tioned previously, the rate of aging gets slower and slower as we grow older. The units of solar time — days, months, weeks, and years — are grossly misleading in measuring biological time. For example, approximately 99 per cent of the growth potential of the human organism is used up before we are born. It is rather extraordinary how far some of us can go in accumulating sheer bulk on the remaining 1 per cent.

The asymmetry of aging is extremely significant to you and to me as individuals, as well as to the physician. First of all, there is a variation in the rate of aging at different times in the life span. For example, at puberty and the climacteric there is an acceleration of change in the structures involved in reproduction, whereas other structures do not show such acceleration of change at that particular time. There is a great variation of physical versus mental, and especially emotional maturation. For example, I am sure all of you have had experiences with individuals with old hearts but young ideas. They are likely to get into trouble because of this asymmetry; they play tennis long after they should cease. Perhaps a greater problem than being old too young, is the problem of being too young when old. Biologic age is by no means synonymous with chronologic age. They are not at all the same. They may coincide, but such parallelism is largely coincidental.

We speak with pride of our freedom, and yet we are slaves to time; it is time to get up; it is time to shave; it is time to get breakfast; it is time to get a plane; it is time to come here to a lecture; it is time for a manuscript; it is time to pay taxes. We have forgotten there are other kinds of time than sun time and chronologic time — months, years, days, and hours. Our ordinary clocks and calendars fail us completely as tools for the measurement of astronomical or geologic time.

There is such thing as biologic time, determined by the rate of living, which may be very rapid in one individual and very slow in another. Phylogenetic time is subdivision of biologic time. There is also psychological time. To illustrate the variations in psychological time: any military aviator knows that ten seconds of combat are the equivalent of ten minutes in apparent duration and intensity of the experience. Everyone of you needs but to contrast an hour spent in a dentist's waiting room with an hour spent in courtship, to appreciate the variability of psychological time. Nevertheless, each interval is still an hour, as measured by that infernal mechanism, the clock. The rate of living at levels lower than the mental (living which goes on below the level of awareness) is similarly variable. The rate of living is affected by use, by disuse, or by abuse. We must remember that disuse is a form of abuse, as we shall see a little later.

Unfortunately, the great majority of us are biologically older than our years. I would like to reverse the proportions and say the majority of us are biologically younger than our years. But I cannot, and remain truthful. It is my clinical impression that the average individual of sixty years is physically nearer what he should be at seventy, because of unnecessary depreciation.

The biologic age of an individual should be the basic criterion for social adjustments related to age, such as when to grant the right of voting, marriage, retirement, and the assumption and removal of privileges and responsibilities. Is it not utterly ridiculous that a man sixty-four years and 364 days is perfectly competent to carry on the immense responsibilities of an important post, and the next day he is too old to carry them? Such arbitrary retirement rules simply do not make sense.

How are we going to measure biologic age? This is an extremely difficult question, because we have to measure various ages, both structural and functional, and to try to average the estimates. Further complicating the problem is the fact that the various functions and structures are of widely differing significance to our total efficiency. Should the thickness and color of the hair or the presence

or absence of wrinkles be weighed the same as visual acuity
or the reserve strength of the heart?

WHAT IS HEALTH?

The measurement of biologic age becomes a very complex and interesting problem, closely paralleling the challenge involved in the measurement of health, because
health and the depreciations of age are closely parallel
problems. The definition of health in the dictionaries today
is sadly inadequate. Knowing that most medical and college
textbooks are at least ten years behind the times, and that
dictionaries are at least twenty-five years behind the times,
we must not anticipate a revision for perhaps another
decade. The antiquated definition of health, as it still appears in authoritative tomes, is that health is that state
of being existing in the absence of disease. A negative and
utterly inadequate definition. To me, health is that state
of being in which all the reserve capacities of the organism
are at their maximum. It is an ideal state, an abstraction,
and, like infinity, unattainable in its perfection, but ap-
proachable.

There can be no sharp line of division between health
and disease if we consider disease a depreciation of health.
Health is always relative. But we must remember that disease does not necessarily imply disaster. There is not an individual in this room who is free of disease in the sense of having some depreciation of health. I have two chronic, utterly
incurable diseases — one an arthritis of the hip that makes
me wax profane at times and that kept me out of the Army,
and the other an absolutely incurable optimism. I am perfectly willing to admit these disorders for they are not
unique. It were better if all of us were aware of our defects
in health and modified our lives accordingly. The adult
who brags about his "perfect health" is suffering hazardous
delusions. As health is always relative, there is always room
for improvement.

Before leaving the subject of the biology of senescence,

I should like to make one more comment regarding the theories of what aging is. As elsewhere in science, there are two opposing theories. The history of science repeatedly demonstrates that, within a year after someone has come forth with an original idea, someone else will present an idea diametrically opposed to the original concept. This sprouting of opposing views is a very splendid thing, because the followers of the first school try to prove their idea is correct, whereas the disciples of the second theory labor prodigiously to accumulate convincing evidence to support their thesis. The competition stimulates research, and progress is accelerated. The two schools of thought regarding the basic reasons for the depreciations of aging are: (1) we wear out and (2) we rust out. One assumes that age change results from misuse or use; the other, from disuse or lack of use. The actual evidence for these two opposing concepts is so nearly equal that we may say the choice between one idea or the other depends upon the personality of the chooser. The energetic and ambitious man who bounds out of bed in the morning with vigor and enthusiasm and yodels in the cold shower says, "To age is to rust out. If I keep going I'll go farther." The indolent, easygoing, lazy sort of chap says, "To age is to wear out. If I take it easy, I'll last longer." The actual data are just about equal. It should be kept in mind, however, that disuse, or lack of use, should be considered a form of abuse or misuse. Thus, the two theories are not truly incompatible nor mutually exclusive. Both may be correct.[4]

But how does this theory and basic science affect you and me as individuals? To my mind, geriatric medicine is by no means limited to the senile, the aged, the decrepit, and the infirm. If it were, I would have no particular interest in geriatric medicine. The senile are the end results of senescence. What is particularly interesting is how we become senile. This morning an attempt was made at defining

[4] Use of capacities is discussed in virtually every chapter, especially the chapters by Dr. Burgess, Dr. Donahue, Dr. Lawton, Dr. Overstreet, and Dr. Weller.

just when the problems of the aged begin. In many respects, the most critical phase of aging occurs in the two decades from forty to sixty. It is in this period of senescence that the changes which will ultimately disable begin and when we can hope to accomplish something by preventive measures. At that time, we have the alternative of trying to prevent unnecessary depreciation or of attempting to patch up a wreck and a ruin later on. Furthermore, there are far more aging people than there are those already old.

Normal senescence is not all depreciation. Aging is not all downhill. Some capacities are improved as others diminish. As speed goes down, skill increases. When speed declines, a compensating increase in endurance occurs. With present accent on youth in sports it is important to realize that all the records for the sprints (100-yard and 200-yard dashes) have been held by youngsters somewhere between eighteen and twenty-two, but that nearly all the records for the marathon run were made by men between thirty-eight and forty-five. Youngsters cannot endure so long an effort. Endurance increases as strength diminishes. As speed of repair following an injury (a broken bone or an illness) slows down, there occurs an increase in immunity, so that certain injuries are avoided.

Let us consider for a moment the ability to learn.[5] I hope Dr. Donahue will forgive me if I overlap her subject to a certain degree. The ability to learn declines very slowly indeed. Studies by Dr. Lorge indicate that at age eighty the ability to learn is approximately the same as at age twelve, with the greatest peak occurring at age twenty-two. The decline is about one-sixth as rapid as the ascent from twelve to twenty-two. It is utterly false and destructive to say that "the old dog cannot learn new tricks." This viciously erroneous concept has done an immeasurable amount of harm, because it has given the older person a magnificent excuse for indolence. It is so easy to repeat, parrot fashion "I'm too old to learn, therefore I need not

[5] This is discussed at considerable length by Dr. Donahue in Chapter IV.

try." I think this falsehood has been perpetuated by three groups of people: the aged themselves, because it is so useful as an excuse; youngsters, who, of course, knowing it all and being absolutely cocksure, justify their assumption by this concept; and lastly, those who have attempted to teach the aged and have failed to discover that in order to teach an old dog new tricks, one must know more than the dog. If the aged want to learn, they can.

The changes that occur with aging start far earlier than their detectable manifestations. They are silent and insidious. The superficial things, like graying hair and wrinkles, are not important. Really, what difference does it make whether the dome be covered with thatch or it be gilded? What goes on underneath is what counts, is it not? The physical implications of normal aging of personal importance are several.

First and foremost is the fact that repair after injury is slowed. We may say that for each five years we have lived it takes us an extra day to repair after a given injury, such as a sore throat or a broken leg. Little Willie, who is five years old, having suffered a sore throat, has a normal temperature after one day; his appetite is such one wonders if he is not hollow, and his energy is such that one nearly has to sit on him to keep him in bed. Grandfather, who is sixty, will require twelve days to achieve the same degree of repair that Willie accomplished in one day. Physicians sometimes find it difficult to persuade an older patient to take adequate time to convalesce, because grandpa feels that the office, or the university, will collapse and go to pieces if he does not get back promptly. It is important for the maintenance of his ego that he feel indispensable. Therefore, it is often necessary to compromise and accept six days for convalescence, one day for each ten years that grandpa has lived, instead of the more appropriate twelve days.

Second, I previously mentioned the lessened reactions to injury and inconspicuousness of symptoms. In consequence of this relative silence, illness is often neglected too long. Delay in diagnosis and in institution of treatment is a definite and serious handicap in the practice of geriatric medicine. Depreciations in health must be searched for by thorough medical study if they are to be discovered early enough to permit of fully effective therapy.

Third, there are lessened reserves for stresses which become apparent with aging. Tolerance for heat and cold, overeating and starvation, dehydration, and salt depletion is reduced. We must learn to use our heads rather than our brawn for defense.

The mental changes which occur with aging are of considerable interest. We have spoken of the depreciation of memory which is particularly impaired for recent events. Long past events are recalled with extraordinary clarity. This depreciation, as Dr. Burgess pointed out, and Dr. Donahue will undoubtedly mention again, is to a great degree dependent on inattention, lack of interest, and a selection of what the older person chooses to remember. Names and faces or telephone numbers do not have the same significance that they had in earlier years. Introductions mean just another name, another face. Frequently, the elderly do not want to remember. If interest is intense, memory depreciation is almost negligible.

Character becomes fixed with age, not necessarily conservative. Who will insist that Wallace is becoming more and more conservative as he grows older? The personality of youth becomes intensified and fixed. A leopard does not change his spots nor do the tiger's stripes get blacker with age. The sanctimonious become intolerable, the opinionated bigots, and the stingy become even more miserly. The generous become so generous that they may give away things that are not their own. The tolerant become increasingly tolerant and understanding. There occurs an expansion and intensification of the character which existed previously; changes are quantitative rather than qualitative.

If notable alteration in personality occurs, we immediately suspect probable mental disease rather than normal depreciation. Much of the fixation and intensification of personality patterns parallels habit fixations. Habits are created and fixed by repetition over a period of time. The older we grow the more time there has been for fixation.

Judgment tends to improve with experience, and the acquisition of experience is dependent upon having lived long enough. But age is no guarantee of good judgment. The young fool will grow up to be an old fool, unless he bless the community by dying young a damn fool. But the bright young lad should grow up to be a wise old man, if given the opportunity, and if he has burned his fingers often enough so that he has learned by his errors. We should learn much more from our errors than from fortuitous experiences.

In my opinion, the phenomenon commonly called second childhood does not exist. There is no such entity as a second childhood. I have worked a great deal with the senile, the childish, the mildly demented, and disoriented older people. Their childishness is a continuation of their first childhood. These are people who never grew up at all. They may have been fairly successful in concealing their lifelong immaturity by living conventionally. As a result of my observations, I have become extremely suspicious of conventionality. As a general rule, the more conventional a person, the greater his immaturity. This applies also to causes, political parties, or religious sectarianism. Conventionality in its broadest sense means reading popular magazines and newspapers and believing them. Such people do not think.

DEGENERATIVE DISORDERS

We have mentioned the relativity of health and the vagueness of the borderline between health and disease. Before closing, I feel obligated to bring to your attention briefly a few facts and ideas pertaining to disease in later years. There are no specific diseases of age. Practically any illness may occur at any age. But certain disorders increase in frequency after the peak of maturity. These disorders, while not limited to senescents, are nevertheless characteristically geriatric. These disorders, by reason of their frequency, their insidious onsets, slow but persistent progressiveness, and immense toll of lives, constitute the major problem of clinical medicine today. Of all deaths 66 per cent are now due to chronic illness, and most of these are included in the so-called degenerative disorders.

Included in this important group are several vascular problems, such as arteriosclerosis, high blood pressure, and heart disease. Arteriosclerosis has many consequences. It may involve vessels of the brain, predominantly, to cause the mental disorder arteriosclerotic dementia, or affect the heart, primarily, to produce coronary disease, or the pancreas where it induces diabetes mellitus. Also included in the disorders of later years are several metabolic disorders: diabetes mellitus, the male and female climacterics, gout, anemia, obesity, the arthritides, and many types of cancer.

The cardiovascular or circulatory disorders disable or destroy approximately ten times more people than cancer. It is conservatively estimated that approximately 600,000 deaths annually are due to cardiovascular disorders. Up until the last few years, there has been a very unfortunate asymmetry in interest and research and in the expenditure of money for study of these different disorders. A study made by Dr. Henry Simms, of Columbia University, revealed that in the year 1940, for every death due to cancer $2.00 was spent on research into the cause and treatment of cancer; for every death due to infectious disorders $4.00 was spent on research in infectious disorders, including tuberculosis; for every death due to poliomyelitis in the year 1940, $500 was spent on research in poliomyelitis; but for every death due to cardiovascular disorders, only seventeen cents was expended in studying their causation, prevention, and therapy. Not until such time that the distribution of funds for research is based more upon logic and less upon emotional and political appeal will we make the progress that we should be making in some of these areas. Today, the situation is vastly improved. There is now a very definite awareness of the recent illogical asymmetry of attention.

These disorders all have certain generic characteristics which are significant. First, their causation is characteristically endogenous. They arise from within, not from external factors. Typically, their causation is a series of superimposed insults, comparable to the various straws that ultimately broke the camel's back. It is significant that the straws, or insults, are not necessarily identical in any two instances. For example, high blood pressure may be due to entirely different factors in each of a dozen cases. No one will ever discover "the cause of" hypertension or of cancer, for there are always many accumulative factors, differing in different instances. Contrasting this clinical problem with those presented by smallpox, typhoid fever, or diphtheria, which are always due to specific and identical infecting organisms, reveals how vastly more complex are these chronic disorders of later years.

Second, the onsets or beginnings of these disorders are without symptoms. These are fifth column disorders that sneak up on us, silent saboteurs that do not ring a bell or wave a red flag and say, "Here we come."

Third, they are chronic, slowly progressive, and characterized by a truly diabolical persistence in their progression. They do not protect the individual by inducing immunity, but rather increase his vulnerability to other disorders. And last, there is observed infinitely more individual variation than in the disorders of youth.

What about the future? What can be done? Prevention of the disorders of youth has given us the greatly increased longevity which is one of the reasons for the calling of this institute. The average life span will have increased approximately twenty years in the fifty years from 1900 to 1950: from approximately forty-seven to sixty-eight. This increment is due largely to the saving of infants' and children's lives from infectious exogenous disorders. Prevention has been accomplished with a minimum of effort upon the part of the beneficiaries because the infectious diseases arose from outside and they can be prevented by control of the environment. Here in Ann Arbor, as in New York, Chicago, and Washington, there is clean water, clean milk, and no more cholera infantum in summer. Smallpox is controlled. But the disorders of aging arise from within, and control of the external environment will not prevent them.

The essential requirements for their prevention and/or early treatment are, first, that initiative and effort be contributed by the individual. We can give health to no one any more than we can give or buy true respect. Both have to be earned. Health is not a fundamental human right. It is a privilege, and, as a privilege, it entails the equivalent responsibility for its maintenance. Thus, the initiative and effort must be made on the part of the aging individual to maintain his own health. Herein lies the greatest obstacle to full application of existing knowledge. Advice which is not followed is useless.

Now that increased longevity has been attained, should we complacently congratulate ourselves and say that clinical medicine, medical science, improved housing, and the like have accomplished all this? Not yet. Though we have traveled far and attained a greater longevity, we do not have longevity with continued usefulness and vigor. We have a ghastly and terrific burden of prolonged disability from the chronic progressive disorders characteristic of senescense. These disorders would present a simpler problem if they killed quickly. But arthritis, arteriosclerosis, diabetes mellitus, heart disease, and mental illness do not kill quickly. The arthritic may become totally disabled for twenty years. To his family, to himself, and to society, he is much more of a problem than if he dies quickly of pneumonia, because he requires financial assistance, and the time and effort of a great many people. There comes a time when we begin to wonder whether the continuous efforts of the fit to maintain the unfit may not jeopardize the survival of the fit. I don't know the answer to this fundamental question, but I think we should pause to think about it. The answer is not too urgent today, but in fifty or one hundred years from now this question is sure to become critically urgent.

MAINTENANCE OF HEALTH

Whose responsibility is maintenance of health? It is yours and mine. Our greatest hope lies, I feel, in research and education. Medical research will be relatively futile, however, without the backing of broad public or lay education. First is the need to emphasize the importance of individual responsibility. Second, education is needed in how to use, rather than abuse, our endowment of healthy bodies in youth. Third, education should be directed toward preparation for senescence. It is truly extraordinary that though we all are in full agreement that youth must spend some of its time in preparing how to become an adult, it is assumed that preparation for senescence is unnecessary. The number of young adults who give thought to their own future is pitifully small. I was once told by Mr. James, then secretary of the Carnegie Teacher's Annuity and Life Insurance Association, which insures university professors, high-school teachers, and the like, that when they wrote to their policyholders: "Dear Professor So and So, You are due to retire in six months. How would you like your pension fund paid, and can we be of any assistance to you?" 75 per cent of their policyholders replied in this vein: "An exception is going to be made in my case. I have made no plans for retirement; I wouldn't know what to do if it was forced upon me." These replies came from people who are supposed to have foresight and who devote their lives to teaching. I think we should be ashamed of ourselves, and I say, "we" because for twenty years I taught medical students.

Finally, I should like to give you the thought that the longer men live, the more time there is to think; to think is to grow; and to grow is to live.

IV

Changes in Psychological Processes with Aging

BY WILMA DONAHUE

Wilma Donahue, Ph.D., is director of the Bureau of Psychological Services in the Institute for Human Adjustment, University of Michigan. She is president of the Midwestern Association of College Psychologists and Psychiatrists, a diplomate in the American Psychological Association, lecturer in the University of Michigan Department of Psychology, and the author of several articles in the field of clinical psychology.

INTRODUCTION

PSYCHOLOGY deals with human behavior and treats it as a continuous process throughout the life span, from earliest prenatal responses to the end of life itself. It is a well-established fact that the patterns of behavior of an individual are conditioned, in part, by the aging process. Exhaustive and excellent research has defined these patterns and their relation to chronological age for the first third of the life cycle. At this point, however, interest has lagged; perhaps the knowledge of the gradual decadence of certain physiological and psychological functions has tended to obscure the fact that psychological growth can extend into the far reaches of later maturity and even into old age. Physiologically, the individual attains his peak of perfection in the early twenties. Psychologically, the same thing is true insofar as we deal with certain isolated traits such as ability to memorize, ability to make scores on intelligence tests, quickness of motor response. It may be, however, no mere coincidence that the biological life function of procreation is served early in life with consequent early aging of this process, while the central nervous system ages the most slowly of all structures. The individual is made free to devote all his energies to the mental and spiritual aspects

63

of living.[1] It is such facts which have allowed Dr. Stieglitz to predict that "the increased longevity of man may be made an incalculably valuable advance. . . . the reward may be the dawning of a new era of intellectual conquest, for man may then live long enough to think."[2] It will be one of the concerns of this paper to explore the possibilities for ensuring continued growth throughout the life span.

Aging, although only of relatively recent interest to modern scientists, has been lamented and commented upon over the centuries. The Latin poet, Maximianus, writing in the sixth century, described the characteristics of old age, such as the loss of sensory acuity, difficulty in recollection of recent events, conservatism and mental inflexibility, disturbances in sleep, diminution in sexual interest, and physical changes in skin, hair, teeth, and bodily shape. The complaints, physical and psychological, have not changed in the last fourteen centuries. Neither has much effort been put forth to understand the nature of the aging process nor to prepare people for this inevitable stage if life continues to its natural end. Quelet, in 1835, made one of the earliest attempts to study development throughout life in his treatise on *Man and the Development of His Faculties*. During the first third of the present century there were scattered papers dealing with the psychological problems of aging. In 1923, G. Stanley Hall published a companion to his volume on *Adolescence* which he entitled *Senescence*. Walter Miles, in the early 1930's, directed the Stanford Later Maturity Research Project, which yielded much of the most detailed information we have on psychological aging. Increasing interest within the last decade is revealed in the publication, in 1946, of the first issues of two professional journals, *Geriatrics* and the *Journal of Gerontology;* in the activity of professional workers expressed through the formation of professional societies — American Geriatrics Society, Old

[1] For a discussion of differential aging of several major functions see Chapter II.

[2] E. J. Stieglitz, *Geriatric Medicine* (Philadelphia: W. B. Saunders Company, 1943), p. 29.

Age Section of the American Psychological Association, the Committee on Adjustment in Old Age of the Social Science Research Council; in the systematic presentations of the problems of aging in books such as those of Cowdry, *Problems of Aging,* published in 1942, Lawton, *New Goals for Old Age,* published in 1943, and Stieglitz, *The Second Forty Years,* published in 1946; and in conferences, institutes, and adult classes in the problem of growing old.

Although as yet the normal psychological structure at different adult levels of maturity has not been systematically established, nor have the specific aspects of aging of individual types and temperaments been determined, enough is known about changes which take place to allow us to discuss psychological behavior in relation to increasing age. Fundamentally, however, behavior at sixty is no different from that at ten, or one, or at birth for that matter. Certain basic principles govern all behavior and these must be reckoned with at all ages.[3] A brief examination of some of the more important principles will help in understanding the effects of the changes in the individual which take place with the advancing years.

SOME BASIC PSYCHOLOGICAL PRINCIPLES
Formulas for Behavior

Let us first examine the basic formulas for behavior. Behavior is a function of both the person and the environment. The physical environment includes such things as food, shelter, books, music, while the psychological environment is represented by security, friends, family ties. The state of the individual determines how the environment is perceived. The age of the individual may be taken as an example. If a group of toys are scattered on the living room floor, the infant does not notice them; the ten-year-old perceives them with joy because he has a need for some outlet through play; the fifty-year-old perceives them as hazards to walking and experiences annoyance at the sight

[3] Dr. Stieglitz in Chapter III and Dr. Burgess in Chapter I also mention the continuity throughout life of certain individual traits.

of them cluttering the floor. It can be seen from this example not only that the state of the individual (age in this case) determines how the environment will be perceived, but also that the state of the individual depends upon the environment.

Normal adaptive behavior may be analyzed into four phases. The first is the state of the individual in which some need, physiological or psychological, is present. This constitutes a motivation and acts as an instigator of activity. The second phase is one during which acts instrumental to satisfying the need or motive are carried out. This phase continues until a goal is reached and the goal response ensues. Finally, there follows a phase of satisfaction or quiescence during which the strength of the motivation is at a minimum. With age, motives may change, but the behavioral pattern used in satisfying them is essentially the same at all periods of life.

An example of a lonely adult may be used to illustrate these four phases of normal adaptive behavior. One winter evening he finds himself feeling lonely. This sense of loneliness acts as a motivator to activity, and he selects a book which he has wanted to read for some time. The book is opened to the first chapter and although it lives up to expectations, he fails to become interested. Tonight it is not satisfying the need for companionship to overcome the feeling of loneliness. In a fit of restlessness he casts the book aside, puts on coat and hat, and sets out for a walk. Thus is initiated a set of instrumental acts. In passing the home of a friend he impulsively walks up to the door and knocks. His friend is at home, and he is welcomed to the fireside for a friendly chat. He finds companionship and thus attains his goal. Later, he returns home and turns eagerly to reading his book, satisfied and no longer lonely.

Frustration and Aggression

Unfortunately, activity does not always lead smoothly to the attainment of goals satisfying to the felt need. Sometimes, oftentimes, there are interferences with the attainment of goals, and frustration ensues. If frustration continues, sooner or later an outburst of socially nonadaptive behavior will occur. If, for example, the lonely adult failed to find his friend at home and perhaps even learned that the friend was attending a social affair he himself would have enjoyed, he is frustrated in his attempt to satisfy his desire for companionship. Frustration is ordinarily followed by some type of aggression which is in itself a need for activity, the goal of which is to do injury. Perhaps our adult did nothing more than slam the outer door of his friend's home very hard. This aggressive act was essentially nonadaptive and was therefore inappropriate except as a means of aggression toward others or things.

Aggressive behavior is frowned upon by our friends, family, and colleagues with the result that as frustration occurs in the everyday business of living, the individual inhibits his natural tendencies to express aggression and develops certain unexpressed instigators to activity. If the frustration continues and if no acceptable substitute is established, the person becomes nervous, tense, and restless and expresses these tensions in anxieties, fears, and irritability. Typical nonadaptive responses include anger, grouches, complaining, tears, and real or fancied illness.[4] The expression of aggression in some form results in a release of tension and the individual is able to carry on in a calm, relaxed manner. The recipient of the aggression is then usually the disturbed one and must in turn find an outlet for the engendered aggression.

By middle age the individual has been confronted by innumerable frustrating experiences, and this assault upon the psychological structure of the personality may take a heavy toll, particularly if early development has resulted in serious personality inadequacies. The type of nonadaptive behavior or adaptive activity in which an individual

---

[4] See Chapter III for an extended treatment of responses to changed environmental situations.

engages is dependent upon learned responses. Those re-actions which lead to the attainment of desired goals usually become the pattern of habitual responses and are used even when they are inappropriate. Personality traits of an individual are his persistent habits to make certain kinds of adjustment. The predisposition to maladjustment lies in the possession of personality characteristics that tend toward a nonadaptive response to baffling or frustrating situations.

We have reviewed these formulas for behavior in order to provide a basis for the understanding of our own actions as well as of others. To put this knowledge into practice and to exercise understanding, one should examine the motivations which initate activity and evaluate the goals toward which they lead. If the goals are unworthy, that is if they are essentially nonadaptive and are aggressive re-sponses to frustrations, substitute goals should be set up and new modes of response learned. A well-spent youth, in terms of having learned desirable modes of response, yields the older individual who is a joy to live with and who is able to command respect and exercise influence on all about him.

Law of Exercise

Before we turn to the examination of the effects of the aging process upon specific psychological traits, there is one more well-established psychological principle I should like to call to your attention. Years ago Dr. Edward L. Thorndike stated that "the repeated use of a connection between a stimulus and a response strengthens it and disuse weakens it."[5] This is known as the law of exercise. It is, in its broader implications, of particular importance to the aging person because it dictates the need for continual exercise of mental powers if we are to avoid brain cells made flabby through disuse.

We may draw an analogy between muscular exercise and mental exercise. After a muscle has been exercised and

[5] P. L. Harriman, *The New Dictionary of Psychology* (New York: Philosophical Library, 1947).

brought to maximum strength it will retain that strength provided at least a minimum amount of use is made of it every day, and provided there is no actual physical deterioration of the neuromuscular system. There is good reason to believe that thinking helps maintain the function of brain cells just as exercise prevents atrophy of muscle tissue. We shall have opportunity to document this statement as we proceed.[6]

AGE TRENDS AND PSYCHOLOGICAL TRAITS

We should now turn to a consideration of age trends and psychological traits and the implications of these for the adjustment of the older person.

General Considerations

Before reviewing specific psychological traits, however, there are some general factors which need to be understood.

It has already been pointed out that aging is a continuing process from conception to the moment of natural death. Although forty-nine has been found to be the average age at which people rate themselves as old, there is no single point at which we may logically say, "Now I am old." The rate of aging varies with the age of the individual. It is fastest in youth and is so slow in the aged as to be almost imperceptible. Age changes at any period of life are very gradual, and as a result the changes are so subtle as to be unappreciated by the individual until after the passing of a considerable number of years.

The general age curves for psychological functions are parabolic in shape. The first third of the curve after birth shows a very sharp acceleration to a peak in the late teens or early twenties; this is the period of increasing efficiency of the organism. A long period during which the individual functions at maximum efficiency results in a plateau or slow decline into the late forties or early fifties. In later maturity there is a more rapid decline in the curve indi-

6 Dr. Stieglitz considers various aspects of use versus lack of use of various capacities. See Chapter III.

cating decreasing efficiency. The first part of the age curve for psychological abilities is very similar to that of the biological functions, but the decrement which takes place in mentation is much less marked in the later years of maturity than that which occurs in many of the biological and simple psychological functions.[7]

Not all parts of the body or all abilities age at the same rate. Age curves of metabolic rate, motor activity, and the reproductive functions show relatively early aging of these processes, while those for intellectual and spiritual development continue long after the physical and vegetative functions begin to fail. This explains why individuals become aware of the physical changes which accompany aging long before they notice psychological changes.

The same abilities decline at different rates in different persons. The patterns of abilities of two people which were very nearly alike at twenty may be very different at sixty, as a result of the differential aging of the abilities in the two individuals.

Age differences and age changes have not infrequently been confused in investigations of the aging process. Practically all studies have been cross-sectional, that is, a group of young people and a group of old people have been compared with respect to certain characteristics presumably related to age. If significant differences were found between the two groups it has been assumed that they were due to the difference in age. A further assumption has been that the changes could be observed in aging individuals. Not until longitudinal studies of the same individuals are made over a span of years will it be possible to establish indubitably the changes which do take place during the aging process and even then, if changes are found, it will be necessary to rule out all factors, except age, in order to ensure that the changes are not to be accounted for by some other factor.[8]

[7] See Figure 1 in Chapter II by Dr. Weller.

[8] Dr. Burgess, Chapter I, and Dr. Stieglitz, Chapter III, treat the matter of aging.

Finally, too much emphasis cannot be placed upon the fact that individual differences in all the traits we will consider are much more marked than are any changes which are attendant upon the aging process.

General Mental Ability

All investigations tend to show that the average performance of older people on tests of general intelligence is considerably lower than that of younger adults. The range of decline varies from an estimated six months to twelve months of mental age per decade. The decline may be more apparent than real for several reasons. The tests used to measure mental ability were designed for use with the young adult who has recently been in school and whose experience has been gained for the most part during the current decade. The young are favored, further, by the fact that the tests put a premium on speed rather than on power. The decline in performance on intelligence tests may be due to a slowing down of mental processes rather than to any major loss in sheer ability to do the tasks required.

Many investigators have found that in marked contrast to other types of intelligence tests, scores on vocabulary tests show little or no decline with increasing age. Other tests which make use of abilities used almost daily, such as general information, spelling tests, etc., also fail to show a decline with aging. Performance on tests employing those functions used but rarely in adult life, such as recalling digits, reproducing designs, solving arithmetic problems, decline at a fairly rapid rate.

There is good evidence to support the view that the greater an individual's intellectual endowment and the greater the amount of education, the less steep is the decline in intellectual ability, other things being equal. The ability of the brain to continue active and to grow in stature is a remarkable phenomenon. Although there is a certain amount of structural deterioration, there is not a concomitant loss in function. Adult mental ability is maintained over a long span of years, especially when the mind has been kept active through continued education and use in vocational and avocational pursuits. Exercise of the mind seems to retard deterioration of intellectual processes. Everyone knows of examples of remarkable accomplishments of older people. Lillian Martens at the age of seventy founded the Old Age Center in San Francisco and directed it until her death at ninety-seven. Determined to learn something new each year, she took up roller skating after eighty. Sherrington, a world-famous physiologist, wrote his most important and most learned volume at the age of eighty-three.

Judgment and reasoning ability reach their peak latest of all abilities. Miles in his studies found that "in the test results for performance not necessitating quickness in reaction, but depending essentially on comprehension, reasoning and judgment; in matters where experience may contribute to the goodness of response; older adults maintain their ability as long as they continue to *maintain mental practice* and intellectual interest."[9] The increase in intellectual power in early and later maturity is evidenced by the fact that it is at these ages that philosophical, historical, biographical, and critical prose is most frequently produced. Such thinking requires a high level ability to integrate ideas in making an over-all evaluation of life. Creative imagination is another ability which knows no age limitation. In old age, as at any other period in life, creative expression brings great satisfaction. It is of concern to some of our scientists that much of the creativeness of childhood has disappeared by the time the individual becomes a young adult. Is it not possible that there is early atrophy of creative imagination because even in the training of the young there is insufficient emphasis upon continued exercise in some form of free expression? If we are to be maximally creative in later years the ability must be practiced from earliest childhood.

[9] W. R. Miles, "Psychological Aspects of Aging," in E. V. Cowdry (ed.), *Problems of Aging* (Baltimore: Williams and Wilkins, 1938), p. 553

Studies have been made of the life histories of many famous men in an attempt to determine at what age these men made their most creative contributions. The age of greatest achievement varies with the field of endeavor. Most athletes make their major contributions in the twenties, scientists in the early thirties, mathematicians, writers, artists in the late thirties, and statesmen and military leaders make their greatest contributions in the late forties and fifties. There is no reason to believe that if minds are kept active through exercise of intellectual and creative imagination, outstanding achievement in fields not involving physical prowess is possible in the seventh and perhaps even the eighth decades.

Learning and Memory

No problem seems more perplexing nor causes greater concern to the older person than what appears to be a growing inability to learn and to remember new material, or to recall specific detailed information once readily available. The older adult wishes to learn, but too frequently he rationalizes his failure to put forth the effort by the old dog —new tricks philosophy. Memory impairment in aging persons may be in part psychogenic in origin. When older individuals who have withdrawn are brought into contact with external realities and become less introversive there is usually an improvement in memory. What are the facts as revealed by objective studies rather than subjective reports? The older adult can continue to learn meaningful things; comprehension of difficult reading shows no change; but there is a decline in ability to remember isolated facts. Perhaps decreased motivation to remember telephone numbers, names, and so on is in part responsible for lowered efficiency. Lack of practice in learning is unfavorable to retention of learning ability. A hobbyist of my acquaintance has recently become interested in growing iris. Although of an age to be included in the later maturity group, he can take one through his garden and name each of the two hundred and fifty varieties planted there. It is important to him to know these plants by name. He reports that aside from having to wait a second or so for the names to come to mind, there seems to be no difficulty either in learning or in recalling them.

Kuhlen reports on a study by Ruch in which the learning ability of three age groups on different types of tasks was compared:

The oldest group (sixty to eighty-five) was least efficient on all types of tasks, but, most important of all, they were most deficient in mastery of those tasks which conflicted with well established habits. The suggestion, accordingly, is that older people have greater difficulty in making those adjustments that involve acceptance of new ideas, new attitudes, or in the development of different skills — especially if these new and different learnings require first the unlearning of previously acquired habits.[10]

The implications of these findings for the adjustment and employment of older persons are obvious.

Sensory and Perceptual Abilities

Some changes take place in the psychological abilities of the individual which are directly related to physical changes occurring with age and which cannot be eliminated or controlled to any great extent through exercise of the function. There are, for example, changes in visual acuity which starts to decline after the age of thirty, when the lens of the eye begins to stiffen and can no longer accommodate readily to different distances of objects. Ability of the eye to accommodate rapidly to darkness declines because the necessary chemical changes in the retina occur at a slower rate. Hearing also suffers a progressive loss in acuity. High tone frequencies are the first to become imperceptible to the aging person. An individual's age can be calculated with some degree of accuracy from a record of auditory acuity. Perceptual ability also shows progressive changes

10 R. G. Kuhlen, "Psychological Trends and Problems in Later Maturity," in *An Introduction to Clinical Psychology* (New York: The Ronald Press, 1948), p. 227.

with advancing age. The speed of perception and the amount which can be appreciated in a single act of perception steadily decreases from decade to decade. Declining sensory and perceptual capacities influence the individual's effectiveness on a job and set limitations on the extent to which social participation can be carried on satisfactorily. If not too marked, defects of sense and perception can be compensated for by experience and persistence in practical situations.

Motor Ability

Motor ability as expressed in skilled hand or foot movements and in speed of reaction declines very gradually from a peak period in early adulthood. Strength of grip or pull shows a similar trend. There is, for example, a difference of six-tenths of a second in reaction time of the fifty-year-old as compared with men in their twenties. It has been calculated that a car driven by a man of sixty-five and traveling at fifty miles an hour would go an extra five feet while he is preparing to put on the brakes. It would appear that young men should be the safest drivers. This is not true as shown by the fact that young adults have a higher accident rate than the older drivers have. The reason is that the older driver brings greater judgment to bear. He is more safety-minded, drives more slowly and less frequently, and under less hazardous conditions. In spite of the slower reaction times, it has been found by several investigators that older workers in industry have fewer accidents than do the younger men in the same establishments. Accident proneness, which is essentially a psychological characteristic, is greatest in youth.

Experience and continued use of a motor skill markedly retard the decrement which normally comes with age. On tests involving manual dexterity it has been found that there is a gradual decrease in speed from the twenties to the sixties and a precipitous drop thereafter. Significantly, older men with mechanical experience are able to achieve the young adult speed on motor tests and are definitely superior in the fifty- to sixty-nine-year age group to men without mechanical training who are of equal intelligence and education. Likewise, experienced women tend to excel inexperienced young men on some tests of motor ability. For example, the average seventy-year-old, skilled woman excelled the average twenty-year-old man on an assembly test.

Continued use of skills once developed ensures that psychomotor capabilities will remain functional at advanced ages. This fact has implication for employment[11] and for the choice and practice of hobbies to be pursued in later life. There is no reason to avoid those work or play activities involving dexterity provided they are practiced a sufficient amount to maintain some skill. Activities in which comprehension and perception precede the making of responses show little decrement in performance with age.

Interests and Motivations

We have discussed some of the changes in mental functioning and of sensory and motor capacities, and other speakers have related the changes which take place in physical capacities with aging. It may be expected that these changes will be reflected in changing interests and motivations. Although rapid interest changes are characteristic of youth, there is but slight change in interests in any given individual after the age of twenty-five. Group tendencies show a slight but significant difference with increasing age because they represent a changing pattern of living. Participation in activities decreases by about 42 per cent, passive pursuits supersede active ones, there is less participation in social activities and a greater liking for inactive sedentary amusements of a solitary type. Changes in personal values are represented by a shift in interest from job advancement to job security, from the more materialistic social and sexual matters to those of religion, philosophy, politics, and cultural pursuits.

[11] In Chapter IX, Dr. Clague reviews several other indices of employability.

Although it is assumed that these changes in activities represent changing interests, it may be more nearly true to say that they are the result of the cultural patterns forced upon adults in later maturity. Little provision has been made for them to continue active pursuits which are within the limitations of their physical capacities, for group participation or socialization. Only in a few instances have communities sought to provide a more favorable climate for the older segment of their population. As the ratio of the older to the younger population changes, more emphasis will be placed upon providing facilities, such as community recreation and hobby programs, for older groups as well as for the youth of the community. When the environment provides the mature group a choice in activities it will be possible to determine the extent to which changes in interest are genuine and how much they have merely been the result of environmental opportunity and cultural expectancy.[12]

As has been mentioned previously, longitudinal studies of the aging of the same individuals have been lacking. Charlotte Bühler attacked this problem by analyzing over three hundred biographical case studies. From these data she has drawn what she terms "the curve of life," which shows a gradual change of life goals as reflected by the changing values of the maturing individual. She found the adolescent period to be characterized as a period of making life plans, of diverse, nonspecific activities, which are preparatory and provisional in nature. The twenties and thirties are the years of specification and definitions in work and personal relationships. At about forty-five, according to this analysis, there is likely to occur a period during which there is a testing of the results and life progress accomplished thus far. For those who are not satisfied with their progress there is a realization that the main object in life is the achievement of certain work goals and there is in this

---

[12] Dr. Burgess, Chapter I, gives extended consideration to activities in relation to the needs of older people.

period frequently a renewed striving to achieve, before it is too late, those things yet unaccomplished. And, finally, there is a period of looking back on life.

Personality

Insofar as personality characteristics are dependent upon physiological functions, changes in personality may occur which are attendant upon physiological age changes. However, as already pointed out, the dynamics of behavior, the behavior sequence, and the reaction to frustration are no different in maturity than in youth. Cultural influences and experiences have resulted in the fixing of persistent habits or patterns of response and these come to represent the personality traits of the individual. There is little reason to assume that these habits would change with age except when forced to do so by necessity or changing capacity or circumstance.

There are no published personality tests which have been designed for use with older age groups and which have been standardized on mature people. The items included on the tests which have been used are those which have been shown to have significance for young people. The items may have quite a different diagnostic implication for older people.

With these limitations in mind, we can examine the attempts which have been made to define the personality of older age levels. Medical data and results of personality inventories indicate that individuals characteristically experience greatest emotional stress in early maturity followed by a period of relative quiescence which continues until old age or late maturity, at which time there is another period of stress.

The structure of the personality of older individuals (fifty to eighty years) has been studied through the use of the Rorschach test. The personality characteristics accompanying increasing age were found to be creative intellectual impoverishment, relatively shallow emotional responsiveness, little inner conflict, and a recurrence of the primitive manifestations of childhood.

Other descriptive studies indicate that women tend to be more emotional and nervous than men at all ages. Married women show poorer adjustment than unmarried women until late in life, and both groups are more poorly adjusted than married men or bachelors. Some increase in feelings of self-depreciation and personal inferiority is present in most older people, perhaps as a result of loss of physical attractiveness, baffling changes in psychological capacities, and the patronizing attitudes of younger people. Also, as we grow older we realize how little we know. In the past, individuals in later maturity have formed a minority group, and many of their problems and personal adjustments are those characteristic of such groups. As the proportion of older individuals in the population increases, changes in attitudes toward them should take place and should be reflected in reduced feelings of personal insecurity and inferiority.

Older people are traditionally described as persistent, as lacking in flexibility and adaptability, and as displaying marked conservative and reactionary attitudes. Cowdry explains the increased conservatism of older people as a result of their sense of inadequacy:

Feeling inferior and inadequate as social beings, they find a sense of security and support in long established beliefs and practices insofar as these affect the environment with which they must interact. To put it another way, the aging person is likely to have an emotional need of finding the world as unchanging and predictable as the infant finds his completely subsidized world.[13]

John Dewey has pointed out that these attitudes of conservatism may depend in part on biological changes. A declining store of physical energy may result in lessened initiative and readiness to undertake new lines of activity. But, also, past experience may make for a more skeptical attitude toward the value of innovation and reform. Ruch has a still different explanation. He suggests that older

13 E. V. Cowdry, *Problems of Aging* (Baltimore: The Williams and Wilkins Company, 1939), p. 467.

adults may be more conservative because they are especially handicapped in learning material opposed to already established habits.

Happiness is another personality trait which has had some study. Happiness is reported in retrospect to be greatest during the years of young adulthood (twenty-five to forty-five) by about 50 per cent of the more than five hundred people studied. A much smaller percentage reported the years of middle age and later life as the happiest. Perhaps with more attention given to the problem of older people, more of them can find the later years of life more or perhaps the most satisfying.

Adjustment to Aging

We have reviewed briefly the basis for an understanding of the dynamics of behavior and certain psychological changes which may be the concomitants of aging or which represent differences between age groups. The aging person must adjust to the changes in physiological and psychological capacities and to new cultural and environmental stress. Declining acuity of the senses, slowing down in motor response, increased difficulty in learning and recall, knowledge of declining intellectual power, and diminishing physical vigor, lead to changes in personality and emotional status. Lack of insight into the implications of the aging process and inadequate information about how to adjust to it results in increased anxiety, fear, and insecurity which may be out of proportion to the degree of change which has taken or will take place.

If we are to be realistic, we must recognize that some changes in psychological capacities are inevitable, and we must understand the implications of these changes in relation to necessary adjustments. We have shown that the basic patterns of response remain essentially the same, that to bring about adjustment in older years requires and follows the same pattern of behavior by which adjustment is achieved in youth. Further, it seems apparent that exercise of the psychological abilities keeps them functional and near maximal capacity into late senescence and early old age. Clinical studies of aging persons indicate that before extreme old age is reached, lack of educability, impairment of memory for recent events, and marked increase in intolerance and conservatism can be avoided or at least kept to a minimum compatible with physiological changes.

One way in which we have suggested the achievement of better interpersonal relationships is through an understanding of the normal behavior sequence, and through an analysis of the situations in which we live, the goals which we are motivated to attain, and the frustrations which we experience. When others seem to treat us badly we should apply our knowledge of why people behave as they do, so that we may better understand their reactions. If this is done, we may find that it is our behavior which is presenting intolerable frustrations for the very people we like most and want to make happy. It is necessary to appreciate that our goals and the motivations which dictate our actions are not necessarily what they appear to be on the surface. The widowed mother who feels rejected by her son because he has married and is concerned in making a home for a new family becomes chronically ill. And yet when circumstances change so that she can be included not as a member but in daily contact with the new family unit, she is almost magically well. However, neither she nor her son recognizes the illness as an aggressive act on the part of the mother which was made in response to the frustration of losing the companionship of her son.

Other adjustments to work and retirement, related to changing psychological capacities, must be made in social attitudes and activities and in the definition of life goals.

In spite of attempts at an enlightened program of social legislation which will provide financial security for older people, it is unlikely that advances in this direction will keep pace with the need for many years to come. Therefore, we may expect that there will be a larger proportion of old people to be provided for in the economy of the country as the number of older workers increases. If these men and women can be employed in occupations which are suited to their capacities, the productivity of the nation can be increased. Adjustments which can be made to changing capacities include a decrease in the number of hours worked per day, a decrease in the physical demands of the work, improvement in working place or organization, avoidance of jobs which require learning and recall of disconnected materials, avoidance of occupations requiring acute vision or hearing or rapid perception of a large number of factors, choice of occupations in which mental or physical speed are unessential, and the selection of occupations in which accumulated experience, skill, knowledge, and judgment can be put to use.

The problem of retirement from active participation in the world of work is one of the most difficult the older individual has to face, particularly when forced upon him while he is still mentally alert and productive. Present practices often cause premature retirement in terms of the psychological age of the individual. It is not possible to retire the mind on the sixty-fifth birthday. New ideas are still conceived and the individual conceiving them still needs the satisfaction of reaching the goal of their realization. Adjustment to this problem is not easy, but the emphasis placed on the need to utilize the fine minds and skills of men and women of mature mind by such leaders as Dr. Stieglitz, Professor Burgess, and others, is beginning to make employers think. Recently, a proposal has been made that there be established an agency which would place retired college professors, who are still psychologically able and often world authorities in their fields, on the faculties of smaller colleges which could not ordinarily afford such learned men as teachers. Many other occupations and professions could provide the same type of opportunity for their skilled workers.

Social withdrawal and loneliness which are frequent accompaniments of old age result in part because the ranks of our friends, family, and acquaintances gradually thin out and it becomes easy to withdraw and live apart. Retrospection and self-incriminations engender feelings of vain regret and despair. There is a loss of the consciousness of the future and in its place there is a feeling of the emptiness of the present, inner unrest, and not infrequently a rather profound depression. The consequence of this kind of withdrawal is inevitable. An unhealthy mind and mental attitude develop and not only the older person but all about him are made bitterly unhappy.

We have said that an unhappy mind is the inevitable consequence of a pronounced degree of social withdrawal, but it is not necessarily the inevitable consequence of aging. If a determined and an active effort is made to overcome the tendency toward withdrawal from social participation and the contingent emotional responses, a good personal adjustment and a happy, healthy mind can be achieved. We should develop a code of maturity which is designed to produce a happy, well-adjusted adult who is developing into later mature and old age. Some of the rules to be included in a code of maturity have already been outlined. It has been recommended that the older person who is developing normally should remain future conscious and have a hopeful, expectant attitude toward it; should take an optimistic rather than a pessimistic outlook; be willing to accept change and to avoid the rigidity of habit; make every effort to keep in things; do some intellectual and creative work daily, entertain friends and younger people; accept invitations to do a variety of things such as attend lectures, plays, concerts, visit with friends and family; develop and participate in hobbies, especially those which permit sharing with others; keep mentally alert and informed through attendance at lectures and adult classes; take an interest in and participate actively in community planning and service.

The community has an obligation to promote the continued growth of its mature citizens as well as the growth and development of its youth. Much emphasis has been put by our committees, organizations, and institutions on programs to develop youth into successful adults and little thought and less action have been put into programs for the development of adults into successful maturity and old age. Cultural and recreational activities suited to the interests and capacities of the older citizen should be provided so that the temptation to withdraw cannot be rationalized on the basis of lack of opportunity for satisfactory outlets.

New goals established during the later years can easily be defined in terms of the capacities of the individual and thus provide an outlet for helping the individual to avoid frustration and attendant nervousness and unhappiness. The satisfaction of achievement remains, at any age, a potent factor in maintaining self-esteem and a sense of usefulness.

In conclusion, the characteristics of the well-adjusted older persons may be summarized as follows: Their life patterns have been found to include plenty of work and a liking for it; strong and varied interests; economic independence and security; good health; many social contacts; hobbies and recreations; living in the present rather than in retrospect; a desire to live life over again; and a predominance of spiritual and mental factors.

These are just the characteristics which the well-adjusted individual should develop through the influence of normal living, and which by later maturity should have become habitual responses. It should then be possible and I hope not trite to say with Rabbi Ben Ezra:

> Grow old along with me!
> The best is yet to be,
> The last of life, for which the first was made.
> Our times are in his hand
> Who saith, "A whole I planned,
> Youth shows but half, trust God: see all,
>   nor be afraid!"

V

Mental Hygiene of Old Age

BY MOSES M. FROHLICH, M.D.

Moses M. Frohlich, M.D., is associate professor of psychiatry at the University of Michigan and director of the Veterans' Readjustment Center. He was a lieutenant colonel in the Army of the United States for three and one-half years during World War II and served overseas for three years in charge of the psychiatric division of a general hospital.

INTRODUCTION

THE PSYCHOLOGICAL problems of old age usually are associated with the readjustments the person who is growing older has to make to the changes which commonly, or well-nigh inevitably, overtake him. These are the changes in his physical functioning, in his work or occupation, in his economic status, and in his social situation. We know that during the last few decades these problems have become more acute in our culture. The changing economic and social structure of our society, as well as the great increase in number of the aged, has emphasized various phases of old-age adjustment. The very real problems in the medical, sociological, and economic spheres are discussed elsewhere in this symposium. What I should like to do at present is to inquire into the emotional impact and the psychological meaning that readjustments to changed situations have for the aged. It is obvious that when anything disturbs the equilibrium of our adjustment we react in a manner more or less characteristic of our personality. We usually repeat our previously established methods of dealing with conflicts or problems. It is also obvious that the equilibrium of different people will be disturbed to different degrees, by the same changes in situation, and that this disturbance will depend on what the specific change means to the individual involved. In other words, the significance to an aging person of any change in his situation,

85

and his mode of reaction to it, will be directly related to his previous history. His present adjustment is the resultant of his constitutional endowment and his physical and functional growth and development, of his past successes and failures, and of his previous modes of adapting his physical, emotional, and social needs to his inner and outer environmental situations.

CHANGES WITH AGE

The very marked individual variations merely emphasize the fact that the person growing older is still the same person, and that the traces of his infancy and childhood, adolescence and maturity, will, of course, be found in his later years. Though his reactions to the various changes in old age will be directly related to his previous life, we can make some successful attempts at generalizations. As we discuss the usual problems of readjustment in older people, we will find that in broad, general terms, their reactions are frequently similar, similar at least within certain groups. There is the problem of physical changes. In normal, uncomplicated aging, the process is slow and gradual and results, among other things, in slowing of activity and lessening of strength, endurance, and dexterity. Recovery from fatigue, from minor illnesses, or injuries usually becomes slower. There is also likely to be some decrease in adaptability to new physical or emotional situations, and there is, as a rule, a diminution of sexual interests and sexual powers.[1] As far as intellectual functions are concerned, there is likely to be a lessening of acuity and some disturbance of recent memory. As long as the process continues to be gradual and the person is able to continue in his usual routine, no serious disturbances in his psychic equilibrium are likely to occur. Crises in adjustment are likely to be precipitated when an illness suddenly underscores the process of aging or when the increasing age is brought to a focus through a forced change in occupation or,

[1] See, also, Chapters II and III for discussions of aging.

occasionally, through such things as difficulty in doing the usual things on a vacation, failure in a competitive situation, or a change in a social or interpersonal relationship. Such minor incidents as the promotion of a younger man to an equal or superior position or a display of disinterest on the part of a younger person of the opposite sex, may bring about a crisis in the adjustment of a person by making him become abruptly aware of the fact that he has aged.

REACTIONS TO AGING

How is he apt to react to this? A man who, throughout his life, has prided himself on his physical prowess and who has constantly, though not necessarily consciously, attempted to protect his bodily self will certainly react much more violently than one who had no strong fears in regard to his physical integrity. So will a woman to whom her beauty and appeal or physical health and capacity were of particular psychological importance. Men or women who have striven throughout their lives from childhood on to balance their feelings of inadequacy by success, will certainly be strongly affected by the realization of their failing capacities. People who have always felt insecure are also likely to have a marked situational reaction at this time. Those who have denied themselves various satisfactions because of feelings of guilt, or other fears, are now likely to become panicky and disturbed and may frantically seek to compensate themselves. Aging, and all it may imply to them, may be completely rejected by them, at least temporarily. They may attempt to deny the fact of their growing older, refuse to acknowledge any illnesses or give heed to any weaknesses. Not only that, they may over-react, affecting manners and clothes of a much younger age, and attempting to achieve successes in their profession, in their social life, and particularly in the sexual sphere, in competition with much younger people. This sort of reaction is quite common. Mild anxiety is quite frequent too, but it may become very marked and show itself in sleeplessness, irritability, or in various fears, especially in regard to health or in regard to the future. Attempts may be made to alleviate these anxieties by excessive care or by almost ritual-like precautions. Depending on their previous modes of reaction, people may extrude the knowledge that they are growing older and their resentment of the younger generations which are making them aware of it, and attach their feelings to others about them. They become suspicious and even paranoid, feeling that they are persecuted and treated unfairly. There may be some truth in this at times, and they make the most of it. Finding satisfactions at their mature level blocked, they may turn to earlier, childish, or even infantile, methods of gaining pleasures. They may act and behave in a helpless, childish manner, unconsciously seeking a return to a more satisfying period of their lives. This may manifest itself in a milder form as an attempt to stop the progress of time by insisting that all things remain as they were, with intolerance for any change or for any new-fangled ideas and with an increased, rigid resistance to any new adaptations. These people may then collect trifles or even trash and store them as if they were something valuable. The realization of being older may be a catastrophe to some, before which they give up the fight and passively submit. They may become markedly depressed in the face of it, further deprecating themselves, being pessimistic, in fact, entirely hopeless about the future, and even committing suicide. Some of these reactions may be relatively mild and transitory. In others they may, however, assume the proportions of a psychosis when the person loses contact with reality to a very considerable extent, or they may become neurotic illnesses often superimposed on a diminished intellectual functioning as a result of some brain damage. These reactions may be temporary and usually are, especially if they occur in association with serious economic, social, or occupational changes, and if the previous adjustment of the person and his previous life satisfactions were adequate.[2] In rarer instances, when the past and

[2] Dr. Burgess discusses adjustment to age changes in Chapter I.

present conditions are unfavorable, they may be extremely persistent and even become permanently incapacitating, in spite of any treatment.

LOSS OF OCCUPATION

Of the changes outside of himself which the aging person has to face, the loss of his occupation is usually extremely disturbing. The loss of a job through discharge, or the loss of one's daily work through retirement, may be sudden and carries with it the implication of economic dependency, unemployability, etc., only too often. In a woman, the loss of her occupation is usually also associated with complete disruption of routine and generally with the need of a serious social readjustment since it is often the result of the death of her husband and the loss of her home. How important the mere routine of some activity may be, can be seen from the numerous instances of older people who find and maintain regular activities of some kind to substitute for the work they have lost. Minor chores around the house, walks to certain places in town, or meeting and inspecting the afternoon train each day assume a tremendous importance. It is as if this regularity itself were an insurance against all the dire but unknown danger which they feel threatening them. But the job itself has much more meaning than this. Our feeling of well-being is always dependent to some extent on how we judge ourselves and how others judge us on the basis of our accomplishments. We derive some of our feeling of well-being from our importance and the power we have, from the usefulness we feel, from the approval of others, as well as from the economic and social status which goes with our occupation. As we get older and the direct satisfactions of our physical, primarily sexual, drives lessen, we seem to depend much more on those things which heighten our self-esteem and which are often associated with our work. It is for this reason partly that older people are so insistent that respect be shown to them and so sensitive to any change which is likely to endanger their established position.

The reaction to the loss of a job will again depend on a great many factors in the person's previous development. It will also depend on how well he was prepared for and how much he had anticipated this particular change. If he was prepared for it, he may still resent it, become mildly anxious or depressed, but is likely to have something ready to substitute for his old work. It may be another, more suitable, job, or some hobby, or study or travel. His reaction and adjustment will also depend upon how much functional capacity he still retains and how much ability to change and to adapt himself to new situations remains with him. A baseball player who is old at forty is in an entirely different situation from that of a factory worker who is discharged from his job or retired at sixty or sixty-five. The baseball player has usually anticipated the end of his active playing days and has been able to prepare some plans for his retirement. He is still young and healthy enough to be able to adjust to some new occupation. The housewife who has lost the work in her home at the age of sixty-five will have fewer capacities for readjustment, especially if, as so often happens, she has withdrawn from social contacts, has limited her interests, and has devoted herself increasingly to her household as her years advanced. Our reactions to loss of job do depend to a very large extent on how rich our life has been before. The fewer satisfactions we had previously, the more disturbed we are likely to get. The fewer friends and interests and hobbies we have, the harder it will be to find a substitute for our jobs. The financial or economic status may make a considerable difference, especially in those people who have through their lives feared and combated an unconscious desire to be dependent and to be taken care of by others. Such people may become markedly disturbed by the prospect of having to succumb to this forbidden desire. Some people may finally give in completely and become excessively childlike, demanding of attention and solicitude now that dependency has become acceptable to them because of their old age.

To summarize, a person's reaction to the loss of his work will depend not only on his previous adjustment, most especially his need for self-esteem, but also on how suddenly this loss came upon him and on what interests and activities he can substitute for his work. During the critical period of readjustment, he will react, depending on his habitual modes of dealing with problems, with anxiety or depression, with irritability or ideas of persecution, with apathy, or at times with sickness. As you know, the reaction or response not infrequently is either a frank and obvious suicide or one which is less apparent but just as effective by means of a so-called accident, or a mysterious but marked and rapid deterioration of health. Luckily, most of the disturbances of readjustment are not only mild but also temporary.

LOSS OF OTHER PERSONS

With advancing years, social or interpersonal relations are apt to be changed by the loss of children, husband or wife, or of friends. The children grow up, become independent, move away, and the house becomes empty. This used to happen fairly early in people's lives, and the children did not go very far. The readjustment to it was then relatively easier. Now people marry later and children stay home longer, and both their occupations and their new locations are often much farther removed from the parents. The loss of children from the home is getting to be a problem of later years and therefore harder to cope with. When much effort and energy and interest have been concentrated on the children, the adjustment to their departure is also more difficult. Too frequently, children have special psychological meanings to their parents, which complicate matters. A mother may have transferred all of her affection from her husband to her children, or to some one child. She will resent and fight against any independent life of this offspring and strongly react to her abandonment by him. The father may attempt to retain his youth and to perpetuate himself and his power through his children and insist on their working with him to serve his interests. He will then become critical and bitter when they choose to do otherwise. These, and some other special types of reaction to the departure of the children from the household, are fortunately not too common.

The loss of a spouse at an advanced age, more commonly the loss of a husband, is likely to result in a marked psychological reaction. It often results in a serious economic change, the loss of a home, and brings forth the specter of a future in a dependent situation. It carries with it an implied threat of the nearness of our own end. Above all, it calls for a readjustment of one's emotional relationships to people. The surviving person must reinvest his feelings of tenderness and affection in someone else and must find other sources to supply his own needs for love and friendliness. At least for a while, life is likely to be empty, frightening, and depressing. People try to ignore or deny the loss of their spouse by retaining the house or the furniture as a symbol of their marriage. They continuously talk of their past life and of the departed husband or wife. We can forgive them if at times they exaggerate and forget some unpleasant difficulties of their past marital life. In their effort to regain an emotional relationship with someone, they may again turn to their children, other relatives, or even strangers, to shower them with solicitude, often interfering and unwelcome, and to demand from them attention with frequently annoying persistence. Their striving to find substitutes in friendships or in the care of children or grandchildren may never prove satisfactory, when it is tried, and their grief may persist. A mental or physical illness coupled with a lack of desire to live not too rarely ends the survivor's life before long.

The difficulties in readjustment after the loss of a spouse, the loss of a job, or the loss of health, are accentuated when our friends become fewer as we grow older. Our own increasing rigidity and insistence on regularity often limit our social contacts. Physical difficulties make the maintenance of friendships difficult. When we lose our jobs, we lose many social contacts. We or our friends are likely to move away and there are fewer and fewer old people around. If we have lost our homes, it is more difficult to entertain and more difficult to meet new friends to replace those who have gone. Younger generations crowd the older people, who are likely to develop a class consciousness and feel resentful toward the whole class of younger people by whom they feel themselves displaced. They become hostile and suspicious and withdraw more and more, becoming increasingly impoverished as far as external satisfactions are concerned and less able to make a readjustment. When economic situations permit it, old people tend to migrate to Florida or California. There the concentrations of old people are high, and this, perhaps even more than the climate, draws them to these places.

The loss of a home, because of economic circumstances or because of the physical or emotional incapacity of the older person to maintain himself independently, brings problems of its own. To live with one's children may be an excellent solution but often brings with it many emotional and psychological difficulties.[3] The parent who attempts to deny his increasing age and his loss of power or independence may not only seek to resume his previous authoritative relationship to his children but may exaggerate it to the point of tyranny. He is made unhappy by any display of independence or difference of interests in his children. He will interfere with all activities and insist on special prerogatives and privileges as an older, wiser, and respected person. He may attempt to exact filial obedience to the point of complete subjugation. Old jealousies are revived and increased and the aged mother may compete with her children for the affection of her grandchildren, of the servants in the house, of the "in-laws," or even of the neighbors. Old hostilities are revived and aggravated on both sides, with the children who

[3] Mrs. Rabinovitz considers living arrangements in Chapter VIII.

had felt themselves rejected or thwarted in their child-hood, attempting unconsciously, or even consciously, to get revenge on their parents. In addition to the usual irrita-tions, this may arouse guilt feelings in the children and dis-turb their emotional equilibrium. When the condition of the parent demands much care because of chronic illness or debility, the problems are likely to become so severe that, to prevent illness on the part of the children and serious emotional disturbances on the part of the grandchildren, other living arrangements must be considered. The struggle between the older parent and his children may resolve itself with the parent becoming submissive, withdrawn, and quite unhappy. The parent may become completely dependent, demanding attention to the point of developing illnesses and exaggerating pains and incapacities. Often this is the only satisfaction the parent gets in a situation in which he feels thwarted, and where his own personal interests and activities are markedly circumscribed by, probably, an unconsciously hostile oversolicitude of his children. What happens when an older mother or father comes to live with a married child, of course, again depends on his previous relationship with this child, on his previous adjustments, and on his present interests. Not only must his own wel-fare be considered, but also that of the rest of the family, most especially that of the youngsters growing up in the household. On the basis of the individual situation, or perhaps on the basis of a trial, it may prove that the best adjustment is permanent residence in the child's home, or that a transitory stay only is advisable there. Living with children will often succeed, but if it does not and if factors are present which cannot be changed, and which will doom the attempt to failure, then living in the home of a stranger or in a special institution for the aged should be resolutely advised and worked for. Wherever the aged one may live, he will fare much better if he has a room of his own. We know that prisoners of war were hopeless and apathetic when first captured and that their hopes and interests revived as soon

as they could hang a picture of their own, or have a bunk
or a little corner which was theirs. With all persons it is
important, but much more so with the aged, that they have
a place which they can keep in any kind of state they wish,
where they can accumulate and hoard, within reason, the
little symbols of their past power and their present security.
Their own rooms represent to them psychologically much
more than we are likely to think when we are younger.

LOSS OF HEALTH

Physical illness is to an older person a serious threat and
a real threat. Certain injuries, like a fracture of the neck or
a femur, and certain incapacities, like those following a
stroke or due to a heart disease, may require a great deal
of care over a long period of time. These are serious risks
but excessive limitation of the activities of an older person
in order to avoid these risks to his physical health may be
even more detrimental to him through their ill effect on
his emotional health. No one can get much satisfaction
from living in a cage lined with cotton batting. Even though
it may entail some risks, an old person with a weak heart
should not be kept strictly in bed nor completely inactive.
Even in illness, some activities must be provided and some
social contacts must be maintained. When, however, the illness becomes too great a burden on the household, too difficult to care for, hospitalization or care in a nursing home
is the wisest thing.[4]

As mentioned previously, older people may exaggerate
their physical handicaps in order to gain, by this means, satisfaction through attention, solicitude, dependency, or even
the expression of their hostilities. This must be treated, like
other attention-gaining mechanisms, by friendly indifference and by attempts to supply other satisfactions. Should
such treatment fail, it might again be wiser for the older
person and healthier, both for him and the others, if he
lived away from his family. He may complain and be bitter

[4] See Chapter VIII for an estimate of the shortage of nursing homes.

for a while, but it is likely that he will eventually develop new interests and satisfactions and become quite happy though at times still complaining.

SUMMARY

I have discussed at some length the various psychological situations one is apt to encounter in older people. This review of some of their emotional problems may leave you with the unfortunate impression that all, or that most of the aged, have serious emotional disturbances. It is true that we all have to readjust in old age as our situations change, but we have to readjust through every change to which we are exposed by the vicissitudes of our lives. The stresses we encounter in old age are perhaps most comparable to the stresses in our adolescence, which is another period of emotional turbulence in which our adjustments are likely to be more strenuous even than in old age. Most of us get by adolescence and most of us are quite likely to keep our equilibrium within fair balance through the process of getting old. The point I want to reiterate is that the severity of our problems, our reactions to them, and our solutions of these problems, depend on our previous life. They are predominantly individual and to a large extent different in each person. Our adjustments are affected by external and internal factors, by cultural, economic, and social situations as well as by the inevitable fact that everything living is constantly aging and dying. Mental hygiene of old age is related to many things which require social or political action. Various educational measures or programs can be helpful in improving mental health of the aged, and social case work can help individual instances. The progress of physical medicine is likely to multiply though not necessarily increase the problems of old age. Many questions relating to the psychic functioning of old people are still unanswered. The practical present-day measures of mental health in old age are part and parcel of the mental hygiene of all ages. The adjustment of the aged is a direct continuation of his adjustment from infancy on. More immediately, our later adjustment depends on the richness and the satisfaction we have achieved before we reach old age. It depends on how well we have matured and how well we have reaped the fruits of our maturity in our relations with our spouses, our children, and our friends. It depends on how well we have achieved emotional security, independence, and the satisfactions of various interests and activities which go with maturity. With better mental hygiene through our earlier life, the problems of old age will be minimized. The better our previous mental health, the more readily we will accept old age, the better we will be prepared for it, and the more easily we shall find pleasures in new things to substitute for those no longer available to us. The problems and difficulties of our later adjustment are largely continuations of our precarious adjustments in earlier years. Those of us who have lived fairly satisfactory lives need not have any fears or doubts about our old age. Our earlier satisfactions will be the foundation and the guarantee of our emotional and psychic well-being in later years.

VI
Religion and Religious Observance in Old Age

By Leroy Waterman

Leroy Waterman, Ph.D., Litt.D., is professor emeritus of Semitics at the University of Michigan. He is known for his translation of the Bible and especially for his interpretation of the Song of Songs. He is the author of books and numerous articles on the Bible, religions of the world, and interpretations of the Christian religion.

OUR RACE IN this atomic age has, without warning, suddenly found itself in an undreamed-of setting of what may be termed cosmic emergency, in which all human values, including religion and religious observance, have been thrown into an over-all new perspective, to which religious thinking has as yet scarcely awakened, to say nothing of having made inevitable adjustments.

No serious consideration of religion henceforth can avoid this problem. It will be necessary first, to try to see what the new perspective is, and then to consider both the adjustments that are called for and what our available resources are for making them. It may be needless to say that there are plenty of inherited as well as natural handicaps to the treatment of our topic.

All the other topics on this program deal with tangible data concerned with the problems of aging. Scientific facts are everywhere available for their discussion. But in the realm of religion we enter an area of the intangible, where there are no fixed data nor any unquestioned standards for evaluating the phenomena that come under consideration. Moreover, religion that in ages past has always been taken for granted, is today sharply challenged. It is repudiated by many as outmoded and a hindrance to human progress.

What makes the matter still more confusing is the fact that in the dominant religion of western civilization, the

99

highest authorities cannot agree either as to what constitutes the content of religion or how it must be observed. Christianity has proved highly fissionable and has, so to speak, exploded into a growing multitude of disparate fragments. These entities manifest a double tendency: on the one hand some of them tend to coalesce again with other units; others manifest a contrary trend toward still further disintegration. These fragments constitute the religious bodies to which one belongs and professes allegiance. They make their appeal for support in a highly competitive field, on the basis of correct belief, authentic rites, authorized leadership, and a select society.

Such phenomena are the end results of highly complicated, age-old processes. The outcome is institutionalized religion, which consists of a partnership between an institution and that thing which we all call religion, in which union the institution becomes not only a partner and often a major partner, but in such combinations in the past history of religions, religion itself has, on numerous occasions, been eclipsed and totally excluded. Under these circumstances current forms and programs of religion can hardly be expected to furnish an adequate basis for the helpful discussion of our topic.

In view of these facts, therefore, an intelligent treatment of our subject would seem to call for the clarifying as far as possible of the ultimate nature and aim of religion itself. And at the outset it may be worth while to point out that all is not well with the conventional forms of religion as they appear officially today. This is not to overlook the fact that the number of their adherents is probably increasing, although statistics of their losses are not always available, nor is it to lose sight of the fact that they have conscientious, able, and devoted leaders. The serious fact is (and it should be possible to state it in the presence of the friends and adherents of religion) that current religion, particularly the Christian religion, has not and is not accomplishing what, on its own confession, humanity has had every right to expect. And there is no other force at hand to do the thing needed, without which at the present juncture our world is in the gravest danger in all its history.

Here is a thesis that should challenge old and young alike. Is religion that important to our present existence? And, if so, is it the religion that has proved inadequate, or does the fault lie with those who have failed to live up to its requirements? We shall try our best to see.

First of all, what is it that Christianity has failed to do? After roughly two thousand years it has gained in this country a little over, or perhaps a little under 50 per cent of the population, depending on how you juggle the figures. That is in a land where Christianity has never had a rival religion and where there was no lack of knowledge of it. It is a disturbing record. This is not, however, its most conspicuous shortcoming, which is rather that its adherents have not observed the two basic laws of its charter, namely, you shall love the Lord your God with all your might, mind, and strength; and your neighbor as yourself. It might be urged that Christians have lived up to the first if not the second, but that is hardly possible. The nature of God as proclaimed through the prophets and the Gospels is such, in His concern for men, that it is impossible to love Him supremely and not to love one's fellow man as oneself. This command calls upon men to do this not just to fellow Christians, because Jesus defined neighbor in such a way that no human being in all the world is left out if you come in contact with him. Christians simply have not done that thing, except in very rare cases which only prove the rule.

That definition of neighborly treatment is so utterly different that it could not happen on a broad scale and not be known to all men. The outside world has never got any such impression. If that command had been kept, it is probably safe to say that there would today be no quibble over a 50 per cent plus or minus pagan population in this land or for that matter in the world. It could well have been 100 per cent on that basis, in both, a thousand years ago, and the millenium would not have been what it has ever remained — a vague, if not vain, and far-off dream.

But this is still not the severest charge against formal Christianity. It is that it has not kept the second command with respect to fellow Christians. Words attributed to Jesus by John's Gospel clearly assume that this is a high standard, and apparently the author did not expect that many would ever to attain to "greater love has no man than this, that a man lay down his life for his friends." But Jesus himself did not think much of that standard, for He once said: "If you love only those that love you, what merit is there in that? For even godless people love those who love them. But I say to you who hear me, love your enemies, treat those who hate you well, bless those who curse you, and pray for those who abuse you" (Luke 6:27).

Christians have not only not kept that command toward fellow Christians, but it is merely a matter of record to say that a flagrant lack of love extending to positive hatred, equal to any such sentiments among non-Christians, has been shown and openly recorded. This is a disease. I have intimated that current religion is far from well, and this is one reason why. Furthermore, it is evident that it is no passing indisposition, but a deep-seated chronic malady that has been eating away at the vitals of Christianity ever since the days of Saint Paul.

I hope in another connection to have something to say about the germ of that sickness. Here we are concerned with the essence of religion itself. Next month the first meeting of the World Council of Churches is to be held in Amsterdam. But over half of the Christian world will not be represented, though some of those not represented will send a few observers, just to see what goes on there. A good many small fractions of Christianity will also not be represented. Those who go will probably not have a love feast together every day. They are going to see, first of all, how many fractions of Christianity can get together and hold a meeting. Perhaps they may be able to hold a single communion service together, a thing which it has never before been possible to do at any such meeting. I say these things in no disparagement. It is a brave endeavor, long overdue, and may great things come of it, but it does give an informing close-up of the world Christian situation that should be a sufficient warrant for seeking the greatest possible clarification of the primary nature of religion.

I have spoken of a disease of religion. And while I do not wish to be misunderstood as regarding religion itself as a malady, though it has been said that man is incurably religious, yet in trying to grasp the primary nature of religion I should like for the moment to think of the germ of religion. We have known the phenomena of religion always, just as we now know, let us say, certain diseases. We know that these can be treated and allayed somewhat, but we also know that we can never master them nor deal with them effectively till we discover the germ, for example, of the dreaded polio. Should not we then in a similar manner seek the germ of religion, in this case that we may the more effectively appropriate its fullest potentialities?

To be sure, this approach does not fit in very well with the idea of original sin and man's perverted nature. Still, Adam and Eve must have had a good nature before the original sin took place, since it is said that all that God made was good. Let us then seek for that and we may find that more of the good has somehow come through than we modern Pharisees, who sometimes thank God that we are not as other men, had suspected, for undoubtedly the main stumbling block to this approach, which goes far to explain why it has not been explored earlier in the interest of religion, is the doctrine of man's total depravity. It has been claimed there is nothing in us of any religious value except the religion we have adopted. But since there is such widespread and in certain cases such completely irreconcilable disagreement as to what constitutes the true form of that religion, it would still seem to be legitimate to try to isolate the germ idea from which all religion has sprung, whether in the Bible or out of it.

First then as to the universality of religion in human experience. The followers of Karl Marx have openly declared to the world that they have discarded religion as something outgrown and pernicious. It has been well said, however, of that philosophy that it nevertheless has its patron saints, its martyrs, its gospel, and an ardent devotion to a cause that professes to be concerned to a very high degree with the preservation of human values; and these phenomena are the accompaniments of religiosity. There are also numerous other people today who will assert they do not believe in religion or that they have no religion. In almost all cases where men thus deny or renounce religion, what they really mean is their repudiation of a particular form of religion, but that does not signify that they have repudiated their religious nature nor that they can do so and remain human.

It is the anthropologists, who cannot be charged with undue enthusiasm for religion, but whose special business it is to study the more primitive races, who have answered our question in the affirmative by asserting that there are no men found anywhere on the earth who do not have religion.

What then is this religious quality that appears universally in the human race and in no other living creatures, a phenomenon within every human being that alone makes possible religious institutions everywhere, in all ages? From what has already been said, it should be evident that the religious urge in man's nature is not to be regarded as something artificially thrust into it or superimposed upon it from without, or that was picked up as it were by chance, but rather as built into the very foundation stones of personality through the process of life unfoldment.

It is unnecessary for our purpose to trace the process, but only to call attention to certain phases that still have significance for man's life today. We may conveniently start with man's ability to conceive of himself as a spiritual being, that is, apart from his physical body. This ability is found among all races. It matters not how this was acquired. This achievement changed his entire outlook on existence and the whole meaning of the universe around him. When he perceived himself as distinct and separable from his body, it opened up before him an endless vista, which capitalized his inmost being as having unending worth and value. From that time forward and forever afterward the values of personality became increasingly more precious than all other goods. This is now summed up for us in the familiar words: "For what shall it profit a man if he gain the whole world but part with his own life?"

One of the greatest boons that has ever been conferred on human life is the growing sense of the sacredness of personality. An increasing lack of this trait is an ominous sign in our time. This quality is primarily due to religion, and without religion it could never have been. Everyone, therefore, who does anything to enhance it is performing a truly religious act of the first importance. Democratic personal rights, which are among our most valued possessions as a nation (or should be), are not founded upon or secured by the laws we have to conserve them, but upon the degree of the sacredness of personality in the minds of men that underlies and implements such laws. Let that factor once deteriorate and disappear and all the laws in the world will never be able to preserve democratic rights. The rule of dictatorships is a sufficient illustration.

The preservation and enhancement of this sacred quality should be a real part of religious observance, though very little of it can be performed in churches. It is limited to no age bracket, but should certainly characterize those of later years, who have lived long enough to appreciate its value, since the measure of its recognition and effectiveness depends on the rank and file of men who embody it. In other words the working level to which it rises in society depends on the level it reaches in the average individual. Lynching, for example, could hardly take place in a community where abhorrence of such acts represents the average sentiment. Too often in such case, while the majority of the community would never participate in lynching, it may well fail to disapprove the deed itself. Racial discrimination that places color above personality is a religious sin. In the face of that widespread evil today, insistence on recognizing personality on the basis of true merit only should be a very real part of religious observance both within and outside the churches. It is also capable of special application to the aging, who because of ill health, for example, may not be able to attend a communion service in a church. Communion depends on having sentiments in common between the parties concerned. The place is secondary. Any one to his dying day, whether in church or out, may continue to be a center that radiates an attitude against race prejudice, and this can be done with the full assurance that it is always highly pleasing to a God who is no respecter of persons. The limitations to religious communion are not so much physical as mental.

I have taken considerable time and pains to search out the germ or, if you prefer, the fountainhead of religion in human personality, and then to point out one or two significant things in life that still flow from it. There may, however, be those who will be inclined to say, Why go to all that trouble? Do we not have a revealed religion that more than meets all our needs?

I shall have something to say presently about revealed religion, but may I point out at this juncture that without this fountainhead of religion in human nature, all the revealed religion in the universe could never touch man. He would be as immune to it as the animal world is immune to the idea of God. But what is more, this religious faculty in man is the judge of all systems of religion. Institutional religion, for reasons already indicated, is prone to go off the track, to become corrupt and decadent. Self-deception is perhaps more likely to happen in religion than in any other phase of life, because emotion rather than reason tends to dominate. It happened in Israel's religion as recorded in the Bible. We might also point out that this has already happened to Christianity with a large segment of our population. These things we believe furnish a sound reason to explore further the basic aim of religion.

In view of all the diversity in religion today, is there such a thing as a constant aim in all religion? Is it a sound aim? What determines it? And how is it possible for men to be in such disagreement about religion if this is so? It is often assumed that the aim of religion is God, that the soul of man has an innate aspiration for the Infinite, that determines the aim. The history of religions does not bear this out. When man awakened to the abiding values of personality, the revelation, for it was also that, was so arresting, so alluring that his efforts to preserve those values constitute the most persistent, enduring, and consistent endeavor that still characterizes man as man. Therein the aim of religion stands revealed, as constant through the ages as the magnetic needle that always points to the pole. All religions from the beginning have embodied it, and in all of them somewhere it comes to focus in that word "salvation." The essential differences that separate all religions are differences in method to attain that end.

Herein the nature and aim of religion are seen to be sound. This is so because they furnish the only basis on which civilization can be held together and by which mankind can persist. But whether they will produce a civilization that can ultimately save mankind, depends largely on the concept of that salvation, for that will go far in determining how it is to be achieved.

In ancient Israel, during the period of the nation and later, the doctrine of immortality as yet played no part in connection with the worship of their national God, and accordingly salvation was conceived in terms of national prosperity; and the values of personality were regarded as sufficiently conserved in the on-going generations of the nation, under the national God. It was in this frame of reference that the great prophets of all time gave their message. For the first time in history able and devoted men, patriots, poets, thinkers, and prophets all rolled into one were able to devote themselves to the main problems of human living. They accepted the proposition that salvation could be expressed in terms of outward prosperity under God. But unlike those moderns who are satisfied to be able to show that prosperity can be found to exist at least for the few, these ancient thinkers were able to see that if the ideal was valid, it should be valid for all, unless it were the person's own fault. But they noted that this was not the case with the majority, and moreover the reason was not that the people lacked religious devotion according to existing standards. This led to the first sweeping critique of formal religion, to the effect that the offerings made to the deity and their formal worship were inadequate, misleading, and of no avail; and then on the basis of the requirements for securing outward well-being for the average man, they declared that economic justice and fair play between man and man were demanded, and if true it must be what God wanted, and since it had always been needed, it must have been what God had always wanted, and not their ritualistic worship. From this vantage point these men were able to see that these requirements must be based upon the wholly ethical character of God and the universe. This is the greatest single revelation in religion. Another poet-prophet went further and said that fair play between man and man requires more than economic justice. It demands the justice that operates in the give and take of personalities, that at its best is called love, and this too by the same kind of reasoning was shown to be a part of God's character. Having made these spiritual discoveries the great seers were able to draw another logical conclusion and declare that such a God could be no respecter of persons or of nations and hence there could be no such thing as a chosen people. He must on the contrary be equally concerned for all men as His creatures.

Here was a unique phase of revealed religion that is not yet fully grasped or appreciated. It furnished the first systematic diagnosis of the problem of human living that could bring salvation to mankind as a living organism, and this is our burning world problem today. It is the glory of the New Testament to clarify and to specify the requirements of prophetic religion in terms of personal relations. For Jesus insisted that the world is one neighborhood and that all men are God's children and are therefore brothers. He also took particular pains to point out that in all human relations the legitimate viewpoint of others should always be taken into consideration. On the basis of such teaching, he was able to say that the Kingdom of God (a very old phrase in his day, to which he gave the new meaning as the kind and quality of human society that God wants) is now in your midst, actually within your reach, already within your grasp, and therefore it is strictly a human responsibility.

The early Christians failed to grasp this thought, and after two thousand years it has still not registered itself in the Christian consciousness. Meantime it has become clear that the salvation or the destruction of our species hangs precariously in the balance. The best in our religious heritage has clearly laid down conditions for its salvation and these are demonstrably sound and adequate. But today, strange to say, they stir no new initiative in a humanity that is at its wit's end; they yield no confidence to a world that is desperately afraid. And the reason? The professedly religious people on the whole are not interested, primarily because the Christian churches from the beginning were not concerned with this life, which they regarded as hopelessly doomed. Thus the blueprint furnished by Jesus for the reign of God on earth missed them entirely and they gave themselves up to Jewish apocalyptic ideas of the hereafter and a salvation based on the principle of the Jewish ritualistic law.

What hope has this type of religion to offer to a desperate humanity today? What way out does it point to the distraught youth of the world? What solace is it to the aged to be told that the destruction promised ages ago is now about to happen. Actually, the cataclysm that now threatens us is wholly in men's hands and therefore a purely human responsibility, in which Christians bear a very heavy share, because of their religious inheritance, and therefore those who rely on the atoning work of Christ for their soul's salvation have no grounds for assuming that this covers delinquency for not being mightily concerned and in the very forefront of all those who are manfully striving to avert a final world catastrophe.

What then can the churches as at present constituted offer to the aged? Is it a sacred asylum in which to end their days? But that asylum can afford no more safety today than any other spot on the earth. There are two main questions now facing Christendom. First, not as commonly assumed, "Can Christianity save individual souls?" but, "Can Christianity itself be salvaged?" This is recognized as improbable unless men can find a sound basis for world peace. This latter also is a purely human problem for which every one of us, regardless of age, must take a full measure of personal responsibility. The second question is not, as usually implied, "Is the Kingdom of God on earth anything more than a utopian dream?" but, "Will the churches be able to see in time that the program of that Kingdom as stated by Jesus offers the one hope of their own salvation?" Religion, at its best, may be stated as citizenship in the Kingdom of God, in which every personal relationship is fraught with religious significance, a potency to bring all men nearer together at the feet of God.

The aging need a feeling of security, not just an easy chair by the fireside, but the assurance that comes from participation in activities that are heart-warming and recognized to be supremely worth while.[1] Today more of such

---

[1] For other discussions of the need for feeling useful, see the chapters by Dr. Burgess and Dr. Donahue.

activities can often be found outside than inside the churches, and they are all optional and a matter of personal preference. Only religion can say what is supremely worth while. As long as the churches assume that their supreme task is to save individual souls out of a perishing world, only preachers and evangelists can do the superlative tasks. But if and when the churches accept the ideal of Jesus, that they must save human society or admit that they have forfeited the main reason for their existence (Jesus said that a bit of leaven must leaven the whole lump if it has any virtue), all activities must then take on a new evaluation. Neither conversion, profession of faith, nor formal worship will be the superlative. On the contrary, the most important things will be those that make for the solidarity of society, for mutual understanding and human brotherhood, by pressing for economic justice among all classes, by promoting kindness, sympathy, and co-operation among all peoples, nations, and races. These will be the superlatives. The churches need to be able to say that these things are now superlatively important, because all that is desirable and valuable in human life is dependent on putting these things across. The whole lump must be leavened or all will perish, including the chance for the Kingdom of God on earth, and the human experiment will have failed.

We know today that when war comes it involves the whole population. All must serve and suffer. Religiously this is a world emergency situation. There are no safe dugouts. There is not sand enough in which to bury our heads. The churches need to be centers that radiate contagious good will, first within their own borders, second among themselves as churches of the community, third into all surrounding society. Wherever there are hot spots they should be there, in support of every effort being made to increase good will and understanding among the nations, looking toward their ultimate organic unification. With such an outlook, the churches should be able to utilize the efforts of all in these matters of supreme importance to our continued existence.

Suitable activity should thus be found for the aging and the aged. Every struggle for civil rights and social justice, every stand for moral principle, every rebuke of vice and moral delinquency, every effort to alleviate suffering and distress and to show kindness and sympathy to those in need should be much more thoroughly organized within the churches and emphasized as supremely worth while. It is a great thing for the aged to feel that they still have a part in all such things. Sometimes just to be counted, which everyone can do, is an important service in all causes that depend on an enlightened public opinion. The churches cannot expect to accomplish their world mission without the enthusiastic backing and support of this ever-increasing group of elderly people. This resource has as yet been scarcely touched. Within this group, as of old, are the wise men and the wise women of every age. Their experience and their best wisdom combined and integrated with the newest insights into the meaning of our existence in this fearsome world situation provide the surest hope for the future of man.

VII
Aging Creatively

BY GEORGE LAWTON

George Lawton, Ph.D., is a consulting psychologist in private practice in New York City. He is president of the Association for Successful Aging in New York City; representative of the Division on Maturity and Old Age of the American Psychological Association; and for two terms was president of the Metropolitan New York Association of Applied Psychology. He is the author of Aging Successfully *and other books and articles.*

I AM A psychologist whose daily job it is to try to build new lives for people over forty. With these men and women, the program of giving them either a fresh start, or a first start, proceeds in three stages. An attempt is made to discover or rediscover their abilities and talents, to free them to contribute to the world what only they can contribute, and to locate for them in our society places where they can be as important after forty as they were before.

This is the way my path shapes itself for me. It is a process of rehabilitation or retraining designed to halt or reverse mental aging; call it "deaging" or "defrosting," if you wish.

My patient, however, is led to see his problem in a somewhat different manner. He says to himself: "To maintain my mental and physical well-being, and to keep my self-respect, there are four things I'll still need when I get older:

"1. I shall need a job or its equivalent. A job is an activity where I am judged by standards set by other people, where I am paid for what I do. An equivalent for a job differs from a job only in that I shall get a token wage, or perhaps none at all. I still shall be engaged in an activity judged by standards set by others.

"2. I shall need close relationships with individual human beings.

113

"3.   I shall need to participate in the work of my community and contribute to its life.

"4.   I shall need to express myself." [1]

The first three of these needs were dealt with fairly adequately in my book *Aging Successfully*. The fourth, "self-expression," was mentioned only from time to time in that work. I therefore have felt the need to consider in greater detail the creative life that can open up to us as we get older. As a companion volume to *Aging Successfully* I now have "in the works," so to speak, "Aging Creatively," and in the remarks that follow I am going to think aloud about this project. As you can well realize, it is a great help to anyone trying to organize and present his ideas in a permanent form to discuss them in advance with an intelligent and responsive audience. So I hope you will not mind if my remarks are somewhat informal and episodic. I also hope my method of procedure will not be too hard on you, and if we are going to age together I hope we will age creatively.

The book I am working on now is about the creative life we can have as we grow older. More specifically, it is about the various arts and crafts that are appropriate to older people. I cannot tell people how to become skillful in any one of the hundreds of arts and crafts. That would require an entire library. Indeed, many a single art or craft or particular phase of the creative life needs its own library. One little book, therefore, dares not intrude where a whole library would be afraid to tread. My entire purpose is to arouse curiosity, to whet appetite, to draw up the curtain on possibilities.

SUCCESSFUL AGING THROUGH CREATIVE EXPERIENCE

Certain things need to be said to people in their thirties and forties. They need to know that life offers fulfillment at every stage, that self-realization and pleasure are possible even in old age, that the imagination is always there for us to use.

---

[1] These needs are discussed by other contributors in Chapters I, IV, V, and XI.

It is to make you try out your imagination, if you are not already doing so, that I am here this afternoon. Your imagination is good. Trust it; enjoy it.

I think it is a big mistake to present any particular art or craft as the one most desirable for people. There are hundreds and hundreds of arts and crafts, and what you will like, I won't, and vice versa. One man's art is another man's poison. That is why the problem of testing for artistic aptitudes, discovering latent interests, is so important. Painting is a most valuable and respectable art, and yet a woman of fifty may prefer to make original dresses for dolls. An older man may wish to do needle point. Another older woman may wish to build a miniature theater. A man may want to make plastic jewelry.

One of my oldest patients, a man of eighty-seven, was recently telling me that he had spent the first two-thirds of his life becoming alive, and now he had a great struggle to keep from making the last third of his life one in which all he tried to do was "stay alive." What he wanted to do was to spend it "becoming more alive."

What I have to say will be most easily received by those people for whom growth and development need never end, who can explore a territory if they are given a map with the paths and hazards indicated and told the equipment they will need. Some people have to be carried or driven to a new territory. These are people who must have guides and servants. They cannot hew paths for themselves. I am hoping to steal people away from soap operas, lonely hearts' columnists, crooners, public lecturers (even like myself in one of my roles), movie houses, radio and television sets. Most of all, I am hoping to steal people away from old age in its most unsuccessful sense.

To age creatively one must believe that it is good to continue experiencing, whether this experiencing be pleasant or unpleasant. As we grow older we may engage in many activities, but the most rewarding of them all is the one in which we express our most intimate self in some organ-

ized kind of way. That means we have to become artists.
Any activity can be creative. Art is an attitude, an approach, a way of viewing experience, not a subject matter,
like painting nor a place, like a concert hall.

One of the most satisfying of all experiences is to be ourselves, to develop whatever talents or interests or ideas we
have. But even if we haven't much in the way of originality
or gift it is good to be ourselves. It is even better to be ourselves in a way that brings pleasure to other people.

Aging is a magnifying glass whose powers of enlarge-
ment increase year by year. As we get older what happens
to us tends to reduce our confidence in our bodies and
minds. Even minor feelings of inferiority are intensified.
It is a great boon to our sense of importance to discover that
we can make something that will be acceptable, even on
an amateur level.

Creative activity carries with it extraordinary potentialities for emotional adjustment. Whether your production
is a masterpiece or not is unimportant. You will learn to
observe light and dark, colors, odors, sounds; you will come
to distinguish materials, planes, and proportions. You will
do things with different aspects of the world of the senses.
This will give you new experiences, new ideas, new pleasures, all without requiring unusual physical effort.

Unsuccessful aging means withdrawal from life. We stop
seeing, and begin to look and watch. We hear but no longer
are aware. We breathe but do not smell. We touch but do
not feel. We dwell deep within the dark well of our loneliness and isolation.

When we call someone an "old" person, we are referring
to the way his mind works, his lack of functioning and participation, his living in the past. It is most important as we
get older that we should keep intact our ability to observe.
If our powers of observation are not being used, we must
bring them out of storage. Since all senses are avenues for
observation, the arts and crafts compel older people to
become more responsive to the world about them, compel

them to use more of themselves than they ever did before. Arts and crafts are an important means of halting and reversing the aging process.[2]

For many years, I have fought a hard battle against the phrase "aging gracefully," trying to substitute for it the one "aging successfully." Victory is not yet, of course, but the fight goes on all the time. I am now launching a second struggle, one as difficult as the first; that against the word "hobby."

Hobby has been defined in various ways: as a part-time activity, as work you would be ashamed to do for a living, as something you do just for your own amusement. Certainly arts and crafts can be hobbies, but a hobby is not necessarily creative. Every year there are hobby shows with thousands of exhibits. I have seen a violin made out of twenty thousand match sticks, and a miniature tower built out of shirt buttons. These projects are wonderful as diversional or chronocidal (i.e., time-killing) activities.

I know a man of seventy-five who made a hobby of collecting abbreviations. He had thousands and thousands of them. During the New Deal his life was one continuous period of rapture and ecstasy. Never did any man's dream come nearer realization. But collecting abbreviations did not tap the fullest resources of this man's mind. It didn't give him emotional release.

Ways to distract ourselves have a place in every life. But we need more than ways to kill time. We need something to tax all of our abilities, to give us mental and emotional fulfillment through an artistic medium, at least as much of such fulfillment as our natures will let us obtain.

Many people have assured me that they had no artistic talent or imagination. They insisted they lacked, most completely, all ability to draw or paint or do anything creative. People who say this have rarely tried out a half-dozen skills of an art or craft variety or made a sincere attempt to find

2 Using capacities to keep them functional is discussed by Dr. Donahue in Chapter IV.

an outlet that was suitable and interesting to them. I have never seen anyone who did that and who then concluded he had no artistic ability. You may say "I haven't any imagination" but you don't mean that, any more than you mean you have no brains or no intelligence.

Artistic ability isn't something that belongs to a special class of people. Every man is a natural artist. If he looks hard enough, he will find an art or craft that he can learn better than the average person can, and one that will give him pleasure in the doing. But he must first overcome his self-consciousness, his fear of making himself ridiculous.

We are constantly using designs, patterns, rhythms, no matter what our jobs. A professional artist is simply a man who uses his talent in the obvious art forms, is more aware than the ordinary person that he is an artist, and therefore takes his work more seriously and gives it more time.

Using our imagination does not mean that we are doing something "high falutin" or unusual. Our imagination is at work, on and off, all day long—when we tell a funny story, or explain why we had to stay late at the office. We do not have to paint a masterpiece to be an artist. We can be one in the way we arrange the flowers on the table, in the kind of meal we cook, or in the tie we select for a particular shirt or suit. An artist is anyone who sees things his own way and does something about it that is communicable to other people.

Many a man or woman will not take up an art or craft because he feels he must either become an expert or remain a nonentity. This is the great American fallacy, the worship of achievement rather than of enjoyment, and it corrodes a great deal of our life. How good any person can become in a particular art need or need not be important to him and to others. What is important is that he exercise his imagination and develop his talent in a particular direction to the furthest degree possible without warping his other interests and activities. An art or craft is an avenue to enjoyment, a form of personality development and enrichment. Our aim should be to become good enough to get pleasure out of what we do, and perhaps good enough to make something worth showing to other people — perhaps giving it to them for a gift, perhaps even selling it and adding to our income.

So much by way of introduction to "Aging Creatively." The first theme in the book proper revolves about the question "Are You Creative Enough?" This chapter maintains that we are a gadget-ridden people, but also a skill-hungry people, that a great many of us suffer from creative malnutrition. The next chapter, "Enjoy Your Older Self," points out that it is both possible and desirable to have fun as you get older. All of our physical abilities decline with age and many of our mental abilities, perhaps most of them, but the one ability which holds up is our imagination. Here is one ability which is ageless. And if we are to get the greatest enjoyment, the greatest sense of usefulness out of the second forty years, it is the imagination that we must learn to utilize.

There is another general chapter called "What Do You Want Out of Life?" This tries to deal with our major wishes and desires and how they change during the life span. Arranged in order of strongest to weakest wishes over the life span they are: The wish for recognition; for response (the desire for affection, emotional security); for financial security; for physical security (desire to protect the body); new experience (desire for novelty, variety, self-expression, creation, need to satisfy curiosity); for beauty (desire for contact with beauty); for participation (desire to belong to a group, to share an activity).[3]

These wishes or desires wax and wane during the life span. The desire for physical security is strongest in infancy and in old age. The desire for new experience is first in childhood and last in old age. The desire for recognition is first in adolescence but never drops below third place. In this

[3] See Chapter I for similar discussion of basic desires.

chapter we see that the arts and crafts represent a socially acceptable and effective way to obtain new experience and thus retard the emotional aspects of the aging process. In our society one of the best ways to receive recognition is via creative achievement, of which fact Grandma Moses is a conspicuous example. There are conscious and official deadlines on employment for older people. There are more or less unconscious deadlines on love and romance for older people. But there is no deadline for artistic activity and achievement.

INTERESTS BY THE SCORE

The next chapter is entitled "The Five Senses and Their Fate." Here is stated another of the basic themes of aging creatively. Art is really the exploitation of our sensory equipment under the guidance of our imagination. When the life expectancy was much less than it is today, our chief artistic achievement was the work of younger people for the most part, and of those senses which are strongest in youth, namely, vision and hearing. Now that life expectancy has gone from age twenty-five in the time of Christ, to age forty-seven in 1900, to age sixty-eight today, human beings who need to use their imaginations will use them via senses that do not decline as rapidly with age as do vision and hearing. The senses of smell, taste, and touch hold up better with age than do vision and hearing. Therefore, in any guide to the creative life of older people we should base our artistic outlets on those senses which hold up well with age. The man or woman of thirty-five who is going to find outlets for his imagination and learn new skills can, of course, acquire some that depend on vision and hearing. But he would be wise to learn those that call on the other and more durable senses.

The more an art uses skills which are largely mental, like imagination, words, and ideas, the more it is immune to the effects of changes in the five senses in the body.[4] As

---

[4] Maintenance and persistence of mental functions are discussed at greater length in Chapters II, III, and IV.

we get older we should try to select arts and crafts where acuteness of the senses is not of paramount importance.

With "Our Eyes as a Source of Pleasure," is introduced the great world of enjoyment to which color and design are the doorway. There are so many books on the market today introducing the beginner to the art of painting, there is not much that I need to say about it, except to pay my respects and with enthusiasm. And this I do. I also point out that with age there is a tendency for the older person to lose his interest in bright colors and to be deprived therefore of the emotional stimulation that comes from their use: in his clothes, home, etc. There may be hesitancy on the part of the older person to employ bright colors, but making them part of his life will introduce a warmth and enrichment that in my opinion are as important to him as vitamins or hormones. ·

The chapter "Doing Things with Sound" is a battlefield where the contest is between the appreciation of music and its performance. The older person suffers from spectatoritis, when he reduces his activity to watching on the sidelines. With so much "appreciation" already in his life, the doctor should certainly not prescribe still another dose of appreciation.

In this chapter on doing things with sound, I do not give reading lists on "how to appreciate the great symphony," followed by advanced lists on "how to appreciate the even greater symphony." Instead, there are described various kinds of simple instruments that older people can learn, the pleasures of choral singing, or choral speech.

Just as I did in the case of the eye, I indicate those experiences that are interesting and will also help train the ear and make it a more sensitive organ, i.e., identifying sounds in the natural world. But art by definition is selection of sensory material plus personal revelation, and therefore merely increasing the sensitivity of the five senses is not enough. One must become more than a passive repository for sound waves or light waves. It is possible for the older person to learn to improvise on a simple instrument, the recorder, for example, or the piano. In that way the older man or woman does something with sounds, they do not merely happen to him. And as long as he listens to the great symphony, and to the even greater symphony, he will not be doing enough with sound. I recognize that in an advanced, cultivated form of appreciation there is an elementary kind of creativity, but only in the genius music critic or in a very highly professionalized musician himself does appreciation become an active, almost creative thing. This also is true of collecting books or other objects. For most people, there is little imagination or creation in the collection of books or paintings. It is only in the biblio-phile or connoisseur of the highest quality that you get some creation.

Another chapter is called "The Wisdom in Your Fingers." This is a kind of hymn to the sense of touch. People learn and enjoy through their eyes and ears but also through their hands. The symphonic skills of those ten fingers, in my opinion, yield a pleasure greater than that produced by any of our other senses. We learn to do by doing, and we learn best to do by working with our hands. Once we accept the idea that we can and should learn through the use of our hands we have the world before us. We can work in wood, metal, stone, plastic, wax, soap, clay, glass, leather, shell, straw, cloth. Artists have even etched on leaves and on human flesh. We can construct models of boats, trains, planes, railroads. We can make musical in-struments and household furniture, or run our own print shop.

The craftsman enjoys the softness of wool, the golden color of straw, the suppleness of wood, the wonderful grain of such woods as elm, and oak, and beech. The craftsman enjoys the variations and individuality in the products of nature.

Civilized man uses his brain far more than he was in-tended to. Man was designed for knowing this world through his five senses and was then supposed to deal with it through the sense of touch, which is why the use of one's hands is such a remarkable adjunct in mental healing.

In the chapter "Arts of Challenge, Danger and Escape" I indicate that the mark of youth is the desire to experience, particularly to experience hazards, with physical skill and courage required to overcome those hazards. To find adventure, to meet with change, thrills, danger, to come close to injury and death, and then to escape at the last second — that is what young people like. Endlessly varied are the methods of seeking danger. But civilized man gets his challenge, danger, and escape in competitive sports. Through rules and standards of sportsmanship we regulate the spirit of combat and rivalry. Facing danger and escaping it is sometimes on the way to creative experience. In sport forms, like fencing and boxing, there is a certain creative element.

The impulse of fighting in the direct form belongs to the first forty years of life. The arts of challenge, danger, and escape are symbols of youth. As we get older, experiencing becomes less muscular. The aggressive impulse has to satisfy itself through sports and games that depend less on the way of sinews and speed and more on the mental challenge; even hunting and fishing may be included here! There are competitive games like croquet and games of chance like card games with small bets on the side, that offer challenge, danger, and escape in a weak solution to older people. So does going to an auction, or solving puzzles. If we cannot hunt or fight in a violent physical form we can do so in a mental form and can do this even in an armchair. Then we shall be doing something ourselves, not watching other people act.

A socially desirable form of fighting for an older person is mental exploration, where he attempts to investigate the world about him, tries to wrest secrets of nature from her, where he seeks to surmount the difficulties of a problem, overcome the resistance of material and make something beautiful.

Arts and crafts can provide "danger and risk" situations, the "danger" being not to life and limb, but that the artist will fail to realize his conception. For older persons, the best kind of "challenge, danger, and escape" is fighting in the service of an unpopular social reform.

It was attendance at a masquerade party at an old age home some years ago that led me to include the chapter "Arts of Enchantment and Reality" in my book. Older people like to wear masks. It gives them a chance to assume a new personality, something we all want more and more as we get older. In the case of the masquerade, the artist is using himself as his own medium. He applies magic to his own appearance and transforms himself. He becomes his own doll or puppet or creature. Though I knew the men and women at this particular party quite well, I could not recognize them by their voices alone. They found it nice, I am sure, to be able to conceal some of the deficiencies that nature had visited upon them. But carrying out the make-believe is what gave the men and women the greatest pleasure as they began to act in terms of the persons they were supposed to represent.

A similar outlet for older people is to put on puppet shows for others, either of the thumb and forefinger type or the real Punch and Judy. It is one way to make a tremendous hit with young people. Here too the older person conceals himself and takes on one of the great roles which old age represents for us deep down in our unconscious, namely, old age as the producer of magic.

I can think of no more interesting way for an older person to spend his time than to put on magic shows or puppet shows for young people. Some older people not only do the puppetry but actually build the playhouse and the puppets and change them from time to time.

Another art or craft appropriate here is the practice of magic. The magician performs miracles but today he admits his trickery. That is why magic will always be popular and the magician always in demand. Learning and practicing magic have many values for the older person, and many older people can readily supply the rest of the story once this clue is given.

There is one chapter in the book which I have done with the greatest enthusiasm, the one on "Cooking as a Fine Art." I have never cooked, that is, nothing worth talking about or worth eating, though the best cooks are drawn from the male sex, particularly the older members of it. Since any material can be used artistically, and since cooking is the most common of human activities, it follows that cooking can be a fine art.

The sense of smell declines more slowly than do the senses of vision and hearing, and therefore cooking is a good art form to develop. Cooking is one of the most important arts for older people. It takes a lifetime of study and experience to become a great artist cook. It is not only a tremendous outlet for self-expression, but has great social importance. There are certain roles in which we will gladly accept older people. Cooking is one of them.

Every community should provide opportunities for older people already good cooks to serve as the dispensers of a high art. There are a great many situations in which an older man or woman could cook for others and earn a small income.

If cooking can be an art form, then eating is equally an art form. Great cooks really call for great eaters. In this chapter on "Eating as a Fine Art" I make much of the fact that we eat more often than we do anything else. If you multiply the average life period of say seventy years by 365 and then by three, the number of times a day we eat, you will see that eating is the most common and also the most psychologically important of all experiences. If any experience can be made into an art form for the average human being it is eating. Therefore, in this chapter I have a section on how to eat an ice-cream cone, a piece of candy, a ham sandwich, for which I got my inspiration from a very remarkable book on the sense of smell by Bienfang.

I have time to indicate only briefly the other chapters. I have one on "Creating with the Entire Body," which is a description of folk dancing for older people, and how to walk and stand. There is one on "Fun Through Learning," which attempts to make attractive the idea of education from the cradle to the grave and of special educational facilities for older people. Then there is one on "Learning Through Fun" which describes the tremendous variety of games which older people can play with members of their family or with friends.

I now get into a series of chapters which offer considerable difficulty and where I am not necessarily satisfied either with the titles or with the way the themes have been developed so far. The first of these is a chapter called "The Art of Being Oneself," which deals with such ideas as self-development, the art of unlocking one's feelings, the art of projecting oneself. Unleashing and transmitting one's feelings, living to the fullest intensity, can become an art form. I try to explain my ideas through the sketch of the life of Mr. Edward T. Hall, director of the Universal School for Handicrafts, in New York City. Mr. Hall, in the way he lives and in the number of artistic outlets he has, is the most creative person I know.

In another chapter I also use a particular individual in order to illustrate my ideas, and that is in the chapter called "The Art of Sharing Oneself." In this case I use a coachman in Lakewood, N. J., who is known to every inhabitant and beloved by them all. I have gone about with this man on his daily trips. I have never seen anyone who is so accessible and so giving of himself. However feeble the older person may become, how poor his vision or his hearing, how little his finances, how deficient he believes himself in artistic talent, there is one art available to him, that of sharing himself.

The next chapter gave me a great deal of thought, and it may seem somewhat out of place in a book on the arts and crafts and also a book dealing with the second forty years.

This is a chapter "Creative Loving." However, love is a function of the imagination and while sex plays a very important part in love it is not the only part and love often continues into extreme old age though sexual ability departs. Love is or can be made an art form. Since with age the purely physical aspects are of much less importance, it is even more necessary that we exploit all the artistic possibilities, all the designs, techniques, and imaginative qualities in the love relationship between a man and woman.

In the chapter "Aging Belongingly" there is a detailed description of recreation centers and clubs for older people. (The appendix to my book will carry a list of names and addresses of these clubs and centers in the various big cities.)

In a chapter I have called "Recline with Pleasure" I have dealt with arts and crafts available to people who are confined to bed for long periods. This is of especial importance because of the large number of bedridden older people.

One chapter has been extremely difficult to do though the entire book has been much more of a challenge to me than I had ever anticipated. It is the chapter called "Arts for Special Moods and Special People." To be active in any art form releases our feelings; particular artistic activities release particular feelings. In this chapter I list and describe a series of special moods and feelings and tell how each mood or feeling can find release through a special art or craft, one for which it has a particular affinity. This, of course, is easier said than done. The professional will recognize that this is occupational therapy with its psychological implications carried to the furthest degree. It is not easy to provide a specific art form for people who are tense, suspicious, sexually repressed, moody, or overelated.

But there are a few sections of this chapter that I particularly like. They are not necessarily the most successful, but the ones that have offered me the greatest challenge. One is the section "Do You Know Anyone with a Starved and Trampled Ego?" and another section "Alcoholics Artistic, Inc.," or "Artistic Alcoholics, Inc."

In this entire chapter, "Arts for Special Moods and Special People," I come as close to grips with the use of artistic activities as psychotherapeutic agents as I possibly can. I believe that art forms are valuable. It is my judgment, however, that neither bibliotherapy nor music therapy nor any other form of therapy via creation can be more than a partial approach to a problem, and that the only kind of psychotherapy that helps in serious instances is the close, hard-working relationship between a therapist and an emotionally disturbed person.

My last chapter is called "Sample Creative Programs," and in this I try to indicate that we should all have a dozen arts and crafts in our repertoire that we do fairly well and that will serve us at different times depending on our mood and situation. We should have arts and crafts suitable for indoors and outdoors, for times when we stand erect and times when we are confined to bed. We should have arts and crafts suitable for our solitary moments and our social ones, and arts and crafts for all of our many moods or selves.

We need not be niggardly about the extent of our creative release. There is no law or moral code which says that we may not be creative eaters, creative lovers, good at water colors, and at playing the recorder, making plastic jewelry, and singing in a choral group — all of these. At any rate, this chapter attempts to draw up repertoires or menus with component parts that have some affinity for each other.

EXPERTNESS NOT ESSENTIAL

We do not have to become an expert in any particular art or craft or limit ourselves to any one medium. As we get older, more important to us than a special interest is a balanced diet, artistically speaking. Human beings are complex creatures who face varied situations and have different moods. We need to have many arts and crafts all ready to tap different sides of our personality.

Art is self-expression; the self that gets expressed is the important thing. We should select our art or craft to make a good fit, just as we select our clothes, the way we comb our hair. The art a man chooses must satisfy a particular need in him.

Every man or woman is an artistic law unto himself; there are no superior or inferior arts. There are only arts that either meet or do not meet your mental and emotional needs. For you they are good — if through them you can make effective use of your talents and skills, and find release for your imagination and moods. If the arts you are considering cannot do that, they are bad — for you.

Try out the creative outlets of your friends. Go to "hobby" shops and "hobby" shows. If there is an art or craft studio or school in your community visit it. Follow up a half dozen activities before you decide. Do not be afraid to drop something fast if you do not like it. There are magazines to read such as *Profitable Hobbies, Science Illustrated,* which has a "hobby" section, or *Recreation Magazine.* The list of books dealing with arts and crafts is endless. There is a plentiful supply of self-instruction manuals. There are many shops and supply houses to furnish you with the materials you will need.

So now you have some idea of what I mean by the phrase "Aging Creatively." The book will have several appendices, one I told you about, the directory of centers and clubs. There will be one on places to study arts and crafts and places to obtain materials. It will conclude with a test of aging successfully.

VIII

Living Arrangements for Older People

By Patricia Rabinovitz

Patricia Rabinovitz is division head of the Wayne County (Michigan) Bureau of Social Aid of the Department of Social Welfare. She is lecturer in the Wayne University School of Public Welfare and in the University of Michigan Institute of Social Work.

WHERE OLDER PEOPLE LIVE

MOST PEOPLE over sixty-five prefer to live in a home they can call their own. According to a 1944 Federal Security Administration study covering nineteen states, 70 per cent of old-age assistance recipients live in their own establishments, owned or rented. The percentage of those living in their own homes is higher (85 per cent) in the general population over 65 when there is less financial pressure. Of the 70 per cent mentioned above, less than one-third live entirely alone; about 25 per cent live with husband or wife; 17 per cent live with spouse together with others. Of the 30 per cent who live in other people's homes, 16 per cent are living with a son or daughter; 1.4 per cent are living in nursing homes; and 0.5 per cent are in private old-age homes. The proportion living with others increases in the group who are bedridden or who are physically unable to care for themselves. Yet, even with those who are bedridden, 34 per cent continue to live in their own establishments, many of them by choice, others because no nursing home is available.

If we are to include the old people who are in infirmaries, who are in mental hospitals because of mild senile dementias, and who are occupying hospital beds not really of necessity but because there is no place else for them to go, we could undoubtedly show need for from seven to ten times as many nursing homes as we have. If we were to judge need for more private old-age residence (not nursing)

131

homes on the basis of waiting lists, we might assume there was need for a great many more. Sometimes there are as many as one hundred names on the waiting list for each resident of the home. (Many of those who have applied for admission, however, may be making a choice on the basis of what is available to them and are selecting the residence home as a "lesser evil.")

ADJUSTMENT TO LIVING WITH OTHERS

When it becomes necessary for older people to live with others, problems of personal adjustment assume major importance. One factor that operates against success is the tendency of older people to live in the past, to cling to fixed routines, to be irritated by change, and to dwell on past achievements instead of remaining effective in the reality of the present. Scientists say that human beings have a great deal of plasticity. When this plasticity is preserved it enables older people to make full use of the opportunities of the present and of the powers remaining to them, to evaluate meaning and usefulness in terms of present needs rather than of past experiences and confused wishes.

In living with others it is not always possible to control emotional reactions of anger, irritation, or hurt feelings, but it is possible to learn to control what is done about these emotions. There is a good deal of "creative living" in thinking straight and acting rationally even when half-understood emotional reactions are involved. Minor irritations gather exaggerated importance when they are repeated daily, and it is surprising how easily many of them could be eliminated by an open discussion. It is good to practice family planning on some matters where no special emotional charge is involved, such as what to have for dinner Sunday and who is to have the family car, moving to more touchy areas of who is to be present when company is entertained, who is to be first to get the newspaper, plans in regard to the use of the bathroom, or whatever the special grievances of the various family members may be.

Calmness, tolerance, and humor are of great assistance wherever we live. The mature person has felt sincerely the impact of such maxims as, "There but for the grace of God go I," and "Let him who is without sin cast the first stone." He has learned that he is not the center of the universe and has even extended tolerance to himself so that he can understand and control his feelings of hostility and not be incapacitated through overburdening guilt. In judging others it is helpful to abandon average stereotypes and permit, accept, and encourage deviations with conviction that the contribution that another makes (even a son-in-law!) may be related to the ways that he is different rather than like ourself.

Some special problems must be met when older people live with their children. Because of the long period of dependency in our society and the emotional relationships involved, it is not possible to regard parents or children just the same as we regard other adults. Both parents and children find it difficult to reverse the dependency where physical or financial help is involved. Children frequently have old hangovers of resentment to authority which make it impossible for them to offer needed assistance, which, in turn, leads them to dominate or to smother the parent with care so that the older person retains no independence. Care of an old person does not carry with it the satisfactions of caring for a child, and there is frequently resentment that this care is necessary. Sometimes this care is offered only because of fear of community criticism. Somehow, it is particularly difficult for parents and children to handle financial matters impartially and objectively. Property transfers and contractual care are dangerous. Even with the best motives it is wiser to seek disinterested advice and trusteeships.

The personal ego of parents is too often involved in attitudes toward children, working against acceptance of these children as they are, without guilt for past mistakes as parents, without seeking to use children as symbols of social prestige, and without resentment of children as representing lost youth. Parents are very apt to get involved in rivalry relationships in connection with in-laws and grandchildren and, on the whole, living with children does not stand much chance of working out successfully for all concerned. Women stand a somewhat better chance of being genuinely welcome than men. Because of their helpfulness with household tasks they more often remain useful to the family longer, particularly in city homes, and here we need to consider well the difference between mutual satisfaction and exploitation.

The importance of solving these family relationship problems cannot be overestimated. It is sometimes deplored that the family is losing many of its former functions, but another way of looking at this would be to see that we now have more time and opportunity to concentrate on the family as the source of our social values and attitudes. It is in the family that we learn the regard for others which helps us to solve our social problems. A generation which has seen two wars and a great depression must know that our survival depends on learning to live more successfully together and that we need to spend time and effort on preventing conditions which generate hostility, anxiety, and insecurity and on promoting conditions which make us more inclined to socially desirable goals.[1]

LIVING ALONE

Problems of living alone center around isolation, loneliness, and the need for physical care. It even becomes necessary to compensate for the loss of family irritations and lack of emotional experience. Many old people would welcome the opportunity to escape the apathy that comes with one day being just like the next even if it meant being involved in the disturbances discussed above. Supplementation to family ties has to start early in life. It is important to establish and preserve friendships, to participate in com-

[1] In Chapter V, Dr. Frohlich also discusses problems of living with others, including children.

munity affairs, and to foster recreational or other interests which are not solitary hobbies but which provide opportunities for social contacts.

SAFE AND FUNCTIONAL HOMES

There are many things in connection with the physical plan of a building which can make it difficult or easy for people to live alone or together. Modern functional design is planned in accordance with who is to live in a house and what the occupants are going to do there rather than according to tradition as to what rooms there should be. Home planners today are talking about "rooms where we can all be together and make noise," "rooms where we can be quiet," "rooms where we can do our work while keeping an eye on the children," rather than using traditional words like bedroom, dining room, and living room. Space should be divided according to activity and who is going to use it, with an eye to the changing activities of different people as the children grow up or as parents grow older. The larger kitchen is coming back into favor, because the housewife can set up a play pen for the baby and still have room to do her work, and grandma can sit down comfortably while she peels the potatoes without feeling isolated in her own room or unwelcome in the living room where the grandchildren are entertaining. Furniture, equipment, and decoration should all be looked at with this critical, functional eye.

Many people are trying to live without household help in the manner that a few people used to live with the help of many servants. Strength is used getting the dirt out of rugs and draperies, climbing ladders, crawling under beds, and waxing and polishing endlessly in an effort to maintain the standard of appearance of a home that was originally designed to be maintained by a whole staff of servants.

For older people with lessened energy who do their own housework, homes must be more efficient to enable them to take part in activities which can make their lives meaningful. In living together successfully, soundproofing and bedrooms large enough for privacy are very helpful. In living alone successfully, time-saving, energy-saving, and even life-saving plans need careful consideration. Disabling accidents, most of them in homes, rise very sharply for women over the age of fifty-five. We need to look critically at storage space, fire hazards, handrails, safety rails in bathtubs, slippery floors, and steps involved in garbage disposal, coal delivery, shopping, and also at booby traps created by accumulations of possessions in dark corners. Single-floor plans are more energy saving than stairs up to bedrooms or down to basements, and first-floor bedrooms are particularly helpful in cases of illness. Where the big family home is no longer suitable, older people need not consider it a backward step to remodel into a two-family dwelling or to sell in order to move to smaller more convenient quarters. A tender ego may fear this is a sign of slipping physically or financially, but rational judgment should reassure him that the physical plant must meet current rather than past needs.

SELECTING A NEW COMMUNITY

In selecting a new place to live it is well to be cautious about pulling up roots too rapidly. For one who has been a contributing member of a community for some years there is frequently an actual loss in starting entirely anew. Some people are guided by a dream rather than by reality in returning to the home of their youth. If this was a farm, the pleasant things may be remembered and the back-breaking work forgotten. It is best to try out first the new plan on an experimental basis for a vacation before buying a trailer or a farm, or moving into a new community. A sound community means one that is close to transportation, that is within close reach of a doctor, and that is not too far from the neighborhood where nursing or housekeeping help could be obtained. Also it is an accessible community in which social outlets and opportunities for participation are to be found. An older neighborhood frequently has more of these sound advantages than a new suburb. In moving to a new community, it is well to consider eligibility for financial assistance should medical care be needed or should income be sharply reduced. At the present time about 39 per cent of people over sixty-five years of age are not self-supporting but are dependent upon some form of public or private assistance, and the average income of the rest is very considerably reduced below the peak earning years. Low cost therefore remains a very important factor.

INSTITUTIONAL LIVING

If it is possible to live alone, what are the advantages of institutional care? It may provide necessary care, and it may offer relief from trying family relationships. One of the big problems in providing adequate nursing home care is the expense involved, usually around $150 a month, and with the limited financial ability of older people this necessitates public and private support which the community has shirked. Increased community understanding and active social action is vitally needed in this area. It has been recommended that hospitals set aside a ward in their own building for chronically ill patients. This would undoubtedly meet a real need, but it does not solve the problem for those who require some care but who need homelike rather than hospital ward surroundings. Because of the overcrowding, most nursing homes too closely resemble hospital wards with beds close together and no facilities for recreation, entertaining, or privacy. Other disadvantages of institutions are: arbitrary regulations for the convenience of the operators of the home rather than for the comfort of the residents; isolation from the community (either through distance or program), and the difficulties involved in moving from one type of care to another as the resident is well or sick, ambulatory or a bed patient; limited recreational programs and libraries; lack of staff with qualifications and personalities able to care for older people with kindliness and effectiveness; too restrictive eligibility requirements for admission; and lack of adequate representation of the group served on the governing boards of institutions.

One suggestion for more adequate quarters for older people is planned housing on a larger scale. Local housing authorities, private builders, or organization-sponsored projects might set aside an adequate percentage of dwellings to be planned in a new project that would be suitable for the large number of older people we are going to have in our population. Ideally, this should not be a segregated project with no opportunity for the mingling of several generations. Old people do not like to be limited in their contacts entirely to other old people, usually enjoy some contacts with children, and have something positive to offer younger people through the accumulated wisdom of their years. Such quarters should be on the first floor, should provide sunny outdoor space and private quarters for single old persons or for couples. A private kitchen is desirable, but, in addition, there should be a common dining room and kitchen to conserve energy for those who are unable to prepare their own meals. There should also be an infirmary with some plans for medical and nursing service and some responsibility on the part of the management of the project for those who may suddenly be in need of some kind of assistance.

Apart from housing there are some other community services which enable older people to live alone more successfully. Lunch clubs which provide one hot meal a day, served in a community building such as a church or hall, and which provide catering service to those unable to leave homes, have been successful in London in a district where there is a large number of older people. Where there is adequate visiting housekeeper and visiting nurse service the number of admissions to nursing homes and infirmaries is cut down. The development and expansion of boarding home programs under social agency supervision would meet a real need. In such a program there is selection of a home suitable to the particular needs of the resident and social case work service is available as special problems or need for change of plan arises.

In order to provide more adequate living arrangements for older people we need to listen carefully to the old people themselves and should not sponsor plans based on preconceived opinions. We need continued interpretation to the citizens in a community so that there will be knowledge of the conditions that exist in family life, in nursing and resident homes, and in the local county infirmary; and we need planned social action to meet needs through governmental and private agencies. When people live in adverse circumstances it is not only themselves but the whole community that is affected, either directly or indirectly, by their unhappiness, poor health, and lack of opportunity to live constructively or to make a contribution to others.

IX

Aging and Employability

BY EWAN CLAGUE

Ewan Clague, Ph.D., is the commissioner of the United States Bureau of Labor Statistics, Washington, D. C. He was at one time director of the Bureau of Research and Statistics of the Social Security Board in which he dealt with social insurance and public assistance. Later, he was director of the Bureau of Employment Security of the same board when he supervised unemployment compensation and employment service.

ORIGINS OF INTEREST IN OLD AGE

IT IS NOW about forty years since the American people first recognized old age as a special social problem. In the beginning, prior to and during World War I and afterward in the 1920's, the condition which commanded public attention was the plight of the old, retired, or disabled worker who was living out his declining years in poverty and misery. The first attack on the problem was a drive for reforming the system of caring for the aged poor — on the whole system of poorhouses, county farms, and other institutions for the aged. There was a demand for modest pensions on a relief basis paid for out of tax funds. This movement attained some success, and there was an expansion of public assistance for the aged.

The great depression of the 1930's widened, deepened, and intensified the problem. Millions of older workers lost their jobs and their self-respect. In the first few, wild, confusing years the problem was obscured to some extent because the aged were only one of many types or classes of workers swept into unemployment and destitution.

As the decade progressed, however, a new aspect of the problem began to emerge. Statistics compiled from the pay rolls of the WPA, statistics of the special census of unemployment, and other related studies, such as those on the work histories of unemployed workers — all these brought

141

out the fact that it was the older workers and the very young ones who suffered most from unemployment. The National Youth Administration reflected public concern with the problem of youth. The passage of the Social Security Act stemmed in considerable degree from the needs of the old.

Late in the decade, it became apparent that the older workers (over age forty-five) were experiencing considerable difficulty in obtaining re-employment. Business recovery left them behind. This gave rise to a resurgence of the pension movement in the form of the Townsend Plan and many similar schemes. The pressure was in favor of reducing the age limits and providing some kind of adequate retirement support, for literally millions of older workers who despaired of ever obtaining gainful employment again. Even the early days of the national defense program did not greatly change this situation. Studies of the unemployed claiming unemployment compensation benefits showed as late as 1941 that the claimants were heavily weighted in the older age groups.

Then came the war itself and a tremendous national labor shortage. With the young men in the armed forces, the older men and women came into their own in the labor market. The older unemployed workers were hired at last. In addition, the expected normal retirements under the old-age and survivors' program of social security did not take place. Finally, there was an actual shift from retirement back into gainful employment. Statistics from the Social Security Board showed that many thousands of old-age beneficiaries dropped the benefits and voluntarily returned to work. Perhaps this development can be summarized in statistical terms as follows: by April, 1945, there were one and one-half million "extra" workers aged fifty-five years or over, that is, above the normal which would have been expected if prewar trends had continued; about three-fourths of a million workers, eligible for retirement under the Social Security Act, had continued to work; lastly, about 70,000 beneficiaries had returned from retirement to covered employment.

THE PRESENT SITUATION

In the postwar period came another situation and another test. With the return of twelve million men from the armed forces, it might have been expected that the older workers and the women, who constituted our wartime emergency labor force, would be pulled back or pushed back into retirement. In the case of women this did happen to a considerable extent — some millions of them returned to the home. But with the older workers, men and women both, this was not the case. They have continued to work right down to the present.[1] In wartime it might have been the stimulus of patriotism and public service which brought these people into the labor force; but in the postwar period, it is obvious that some other factors have been at work. Plainly speaking, these older workers clearly prefer to remain in the labor force as long as job opportunities are open to them.

All these recent facts might be taken to indicate that there is no particular problem of aging and employability. Has the problem disappeared? My answer is that it has not. It is partly obscured at the moment by the high employment of our postwar prosperity. The fact that so many older workers are now employed should not blind us to some of the underlying long-range problems. Are these workers happily placed? Are they productive? Do their employers rate them highly?

The answer to these and other questions will be speedily forthcoming, I believe, when our economy "catches up" with its wartime shortages and readjustments to a more normal postwar level. (I am talking only about a readjustment, not a major business depression.) In such a readjustment, I venture to guess that the unemployment of older workers will again become a serious social problem. Many of them will be laid off in the early stages of an employment downturn, and their numbers (unemployed) will increase persistently during any period of moderate busi-

[1] See Chapter X for other statistics on the size of the labor force.

ness activity. Furthermore, they will find it more and more difficult to get back into satisfactory jobs. Their unemployment periods will be prolonged and persistent. Then the nation will find itself face to face with a stubborn and difficult problem of great dimensions. Since the proportion of older workers in the labor force is growing steadily, this development will create new social, economic, and political problems which will test our ingenuity as a nation to solve.

SHALL THEY RETIRE?

At first thought it might seem that this is simply a problem of individual preference for work or retirement. In a free democratic society let those who want to work continue to do so, and let those retire who do not wish to continue to work. Of course, as has been discussed elsewhere during this Institute, this would mean some reasonably adequate provision for retirement. During the depression years one of the reasons advanced for the passage of social security legislation was that it would encourage retirement of older workers, and thus make room for younger men. The actual scale of old-age benefits, however, has never provided a reasonable choice to the older workers. Most of the retirements under old-age insurance have been forced upon the worker by previous unemployment. In a special field survey conducted by old-age and survivors' insurance in 1941-42, only about 5 per cent of the men receiving old-age benefits said that they retired and filed for benefits while they were in good health. More than half had been laid off by employers, and about one-third retired because of illness or failing health.

With the higher costs of living existing today, these benefits are even less of an inducement to retire. Under the old-age and survivors' insurance program benefits for a retired worker and his wife now average less than $500 a year. Yet the Social Security Administration has estimated that a family budget for an older couple, at a modest but adequate level of living in eight selected cities, would range from

$1,365 in Houston, Texas, to $1,767 in Washington, D.C. This was at June, 1947, prices, and the consumers' price index of the Bureau of Labor Statistics has risen since that time.

With this is the fact that only a very small minority of the aged can count on income from property or some other source sufficient to close this gap. Thus, retirement for the great majority of workers today would require an extremely low level of living, dependence upon children or other relatives, or public assistance. It seems clear that a nation committed to an adequate retirement system will certainly raise the scale of benefits and bring them more nearly into reasonable relationship with the minimum earning power of older workers. If and when it is done, some of the older workers, at least, will be free to make a reasonable choice as to work or retirement. Some will continue to work, others will voluntarily retire.

But let us not be under any illusions that such an adequate program of old-age insurance benefits would meet the problem. What age are we thinking about? Men eligible for retirement at age sixty-five and perhaps women at sixty? This will not begin to touch the problem of the millions of workers age forty-five to sixty-four, men and women both. Pushing the age limit for men down to age sixty would create tremendous financial problems, even for a rich nation like the United States. To talk about retirement ages of fifty-five, fifty, or below is literally fantastic. We would be condemning the nation to a poverty standard of living for all if any such goal were attempted.

As a matter of fact, this is the form which the issue may take politically. If truly adequate and reasonable benefits are established for the oldest workers (over sixty-five), then there will be pressure to lower the age limits and bring in the unemployed in the next lower age groups. In times of severe unemployment the numbers of these persons may be so great as to constitute a powerful social and political force.[2]

[2] Dr. Kidd's discussion in Chapter X should be read with regard to retirement age and cost of benefits.

ARE THEY EMPLOYABLE?

So we are brought to the other solutions: What are the possibilities of these nearly old workers continuing in gainful employment? In future decades they will constitute a large labor force which could be employed successfully to raise the standard of living of the whole population. As an economic policy, these nearly old should not be looking forward to speedy retirement but rather to continued productive work. What is the chance of achieving this as a national policy?

The first question that arises in this connection is the true employability of these workers. How do they actually succeed in the jobs they are able to hold? A recent study by the Bureau of Labor Statistics provides us some partial answers to this question.

During the war years the Bureau of Labor Statistics, at the request of the Veterans Administration, made an extended study of the work performance of physically impaired workers.[3] The purpose of that particular study was to analyze the effect of various types of physical impairment upon the worker's capacity to hold a job. In making that study the bureau measured the physically impaired workers against a control group of normal workers. Then, as a by-product, the bureau made a study of this control group from the point of view of age. Some of the results of this study have been published in the *Monthly Labor Review* for July, 1948.[4] I shall review briefly for you the salient facts discovered in this study.

First, the records show that absenteeism is generally less frequent among the older workers. Among the men absenteeism was highest (5.2 days lost per one hundred scheduled work days) among the youngsters under twenty, after which it declined steadily until the low point was reached in the group age of fifty-five to fifty-nine (2.8 days lost). There was

[3] *Monthly Labor Rev.*, Jan., 1948.

[4] Max D. Kossoris, "Absenteeism in Injury Experiences of Older Workers," *Monthly Labor Rev.*, July, 1948.

a slight increase in the rate for men over sixty-five, but even this compared favorably to the absenteeism of the men in their thirties and forties, and was considerably less than for men in their twenties and teens. Likewise, among the women the lowest absentee rate was in the group of fifty-five to fifty-nine. It is most important to note that these rates were obtained in a period of full employment when large numbers of these older workers were on the job.

With respect to work injuries the study indicates that older workers have a record that is at least as good and even somewhat better than for younger workers. Disabling injuries are those which require an employee either to sustain a permanent impairment or to be disabled for work for at least one full shift. For this type of injury the frequency rate (per million hours worked) was 9.7 for all age groups, but generally lower than this for workers over fifty, with a rate of 7.8 for those from fifty to fifty-four, and a rate of 10.1 for those of fifty-five to fifty-nine. No age group over fifty had a rate as high as the group of thirty-five to forty-four years. Nondisabling injuries are those which usually require only first aid. With respect to these, the rates are highest for workers in the twenties and lowest for those over forty. The frequency rate for all groups of workers over fifty range from a half to a quarter of the rate for workers in the twenties. On the other hand, it was noted in the study that the older workers require more time for their injuries to heal — the average number of days which the disability lasted was longer in the older groups.

Lastly, the study recorded the medical visits made by employees for minor aches and pains not directly related to work accidents: difficulties such as headaches, colds, digestive discomforts, and menstrual pains. Again the record shows that, among both men and women, the older workers made fewer medical welfare visits than did those in the younger age groups.

The conclusions we can draw from this study are simply that older workers in certain very tangible respects can hold up their end of the work so far as absenteeism, accidents, and various disabilities are concerned. This seems to show that some of the prejudice against older workers is not based on fact. There seems to be clear evidence of a greater willingness and zeal to keep on the job.

Of course, this study provides only a partial answer to our question. There are still other areas of employability which require exploration. The most obvious one is productivity. Do these workers keep up the pace and produce as well as do the younger groups The Bureau was not able to obtain any comparison of output by age groups. Such data would be difficult to obtain because comparison would have to be based on appreciably large numbers of workers in the same or similar jobs — a situation that would be hard to find. More work will have to be done to determine whether low productivity or poor quality output lessens the employability of older workers.

There are some studies from the United States Public Health Service which provide some hints on this side of the problem. These studies seem to show that the onset of chronic disabilities is a gradual process; it is not concentrated in any particular age group. For example, the National Health Survey (1935-36) showed a progressive increase in the incidence of chronic disabilities, from twenty-seven per hundred in the age group forty-five to fifty-four to thirty-four per hundred for the group fifty-five to sixty-four, and to fifty-one per hundred among those sixty-five to seventy-four years old. Chronic disability in this sense is not directly comparable with inability to work. Many persons with disabilities or impairments may continue to work for years. The data, however, are indicative of the process of slowing down and deterioration of the human organism with age.

Yet, it is noteworthy that even among persons sixty-five to seventy-four years of age almost half were not affected by any chronic disability or impairment. Moreover, only a small proportion of the population, even at the upper age extreme, are so disabled that they are clearly "permanently disabled" for all employment. Thus, even in the age group sixty-five to seventy-four, only five out of every one hundred persons were classified as invalids (that is, disabled for twelve months or more).

Recently, I noticed a newspaper report of a medical staff conference at the De Courcy Clinic in Cincinnati, Ohio, in which the medical specialists came to the startling conclusion that "years alone have no effect in bringing about degenerative disorders. Anyone who thinks that because he or she is getting along in years, loss of vigor, debilities, or degenerative disorders should be experienced, is suffering from a 'time neurosis' which may be more effective than physical conditions in producing the effects he fears." In other words, you are old only because you think you are. They go on to say:

All those who develop a time neurosis subscribe to the prevalent superstition that time is in some way a poison exerting a mysterious cumulative action. The obsession itself may be the cause of definitely premature aging. Confidence and hope are diminished; continual worry decreases efficiency and increases nervousness and irritability. Life assumes a somber hue. Imaginary symptoms are noted with increasing frequency. The mind or the heart may seem to be failing. Morbid attention is given to every phase of physiology of which the patient may be aware. Morbid conditions then ensue. — New York Herald-Tribune, July 18, 1948.

I think we must all know personally many older people who fit this picture — who worry themselves into ill-health because of imaginary fears and handicaps.

Where does all this leave us? I suggest that the present state of our knowledge (which is admittedly incomplete) points to the following general conclusions: (1) Many old people retain their full faculties and vigor to an advanced age and can successfully hold a job or practice an occupation far beyond the arbitrary time of retirement; (2) many other old people experience some accident, disability, debility, or simple decline in powers which lessens their capacity for their previous jobs but which does not make them at all unemployable; (3) some old people (an actual minority) become permanently ill or disabled (not at any fixed age but at varying ages) so that they cannot or should not be required to earn their own living.

What then is the basic unsolved problem of aging and employability? It is the problem of class (2) above — the workers with declining powers who continue for years to possess a high degree of employability. These workers could remain in employment if there could be a gradual readjustment of the work to fit their changing capacities.

This is not the way it is generally done in industry today. There are notable exceptions, of course, and in many firms and occupations quiet adaptation of the job to advancing age occurs unobtrusively. But in the main the worker who is growing old fights vigorously to retain his position and status on the job until the final break comes — then he is laid off, cannot get another job, and is mentally and physically crushed.

This struggle of the older worker to hold his place is reflected strongly in trade union policies. Efforts are made in the collective bargaining agreements with employers to obtain clauses providing to older workers security of employment and protection of earning opportunities.

The most important results of these union efforts are seniority rules and practices which afford protection to employees in accordance with the length of service. The seniority principle in general means that preference in promotions, better assignments, avoidance of layoffs, and reemployment after layoff depend primarily on the number of years of service. Since years of service are very closely related to age, the observance of seniority rights implies preferential treatment for the older worker.

In the building trades, particularly, agreements sometimes specifically require employment of a certain number of older persons. The requirement is most frequently that there shall be at least one superannuated worker, a man of the age of fifty-five or over, among five, seven, or ten journeymen employed. The following clause is illustrative: "On jobs where seven or more members of the union are employed one member of more than sixty years of age shall be employed for every seven younger members."

Occasionally, agreements contain prohibitions on termination of employment because of age, as in the following clause: "The Company agrees that no employee's service will be terminated solely because of age."

A few agreements specifically prohibit any restrictions as to age limits in the hiring of new employees, as in the following clause: "The Company agrees that there shall be no maximum age limit in the hiring of men."

Although unions insist on rigid adherence to the wage standards set forth in the agreement for all regular employees, a tolerance is sometimes allowed for aged or handicapped workers. If these employees cannot maintain the production standards, lower rates may be negotiated at the time the agreement is signed or subsequently as cases arise. Some agreements specify a special minimum rate below which wages of substandard workers may not fall. Aged workers and those who for other reasons are unable to perform their regular work are sometimes assured transfers to other types of work. An illustrative clause dealing with this problem follows:

An employee who has given long, faithful service and has become unable to handle heavy work or work required in his classification to advantage, shall be given preference in such work as he may be able to perform at a commensurate rate of pay agreed to between the Company and the union.

The difficulty is that these protections through collective bargaining agreements or company rules generally break down in times of severe unemployment. Businesses fail; new inventions make old occupations obsolete; layoffs of older workers do occur; attachments to previous jobs are broken. The constructive long-run solution of the problem is the development of jobs and occupations which can be adequately filled by older workers.

In this respect the situation is not getting better. Agriculture is an industry which always gave substantial employment to even the very old. There are always jobs around a farm which a partly employable person can do. In the cities the self-employed worker (whether a business proprietor, a professional, or an artisan) is in a better position to continue his activity while "tapering off" his work in his old age. The proportion of employers and self-employed workers among urban men in 1940 rose sharply from less than one-fifth of the total among men forty-five to fifty-four years of age to two-fifths among men seventy-five years or over. Only a minority of the older industrial workers, however, fall in those classes of occupation which generally give rise to self-employment.

POSSIBILITIES FOR EMPLOYMENT

The major attack on the problem will have to come within industry itself, which employs the vast proportion of the labor force. With agriculture declining (in employment) and urban self-employed being limited in numbers, the real job is to discover how industry itself can provide gradual self-adjusting employment for older workers.

I have no intention here of saddling businessmen and employers generally with this problem. Industry has a responsibility, but it is not alone in this responsibility. The worker himself has a distinct responsibility of his own — to accept different kinds of work, to accede willingly to changes in pay for such work, and to undertake any training or retraining which might be required to keep up his employability. The community itself, with all its numerous agencies (which I shall not take the time here to mention) has a great responsibility for providing the facilities for assisting industry and the workers to make these adaptations. This means training and retraining facilities, an adequate public placement service, educational opportunities for older people, and all the other kinds of professional assistance which will have to be provided if this job is to be accomplished on a nationwide scale. This will be one of the great future challenges to the schools of the nation.

All this may seem to those who are "realists" much too visionary and idealistic. I do not believe it is. The choice which this nation will face in the next few decades is a very hard one. If unemployment and destitution are chronic among the millions of older men and women in this country, they will be numerous enough to force us to some kind of social action. What we may get from such pressures may be very unsatisfactory — socially, economically, and politically. If we can use these millions of willing and able men and women as part of the productive labor force of the nation, we may raise the standard of living of Americans to levels far beyond our present dreams. In the process we shall also be helping to make ourselves a happier people and a much better economic society.

X

Economic Security for Older Persons[1]

By Charles V. Kidd

Charles V. Kidd is an economist with the Council of Economic Advisers and is a specialist in the field of social security. He has been a member of the President's Scientific Research Board and chief of the Manpower Stabilization Section of the War Manpower Commission. He is the author of numerous articles on social insurance and employment stabilization.

INTRODUCTION

THE ECONOMIC problems involved in providing economic security to aged people are of such complexity and magnitude that they affect the whole country. For this reason, they can be examined most profitably in the setting of the resources of the entire economy and of the distribution of resources among different population and income groups.

When economic security for the entire population — or any large group of the population, such as aged people — is considered, the questions involved are entirely different from those involved in providing economic security for individuals. If an individual is given an assured income of $10,000 a year, he and his family will have a high degree of economic security. But the larger the group to which income is given, the less the members of that group would gain. Finally, if every head of a household were given an assured income of $10,000 a year, it is quite probable that no one would be any better off than he was before.

The reason for this is that economic security is provided for the population as a whole not by money income but by goods. It is what money can buy, rather than the money itself, that determines the level of economic well-being for individuals, groups, and the country.

[1] The opinions expressed in this paper are those of the author and not necessarily those of the Council of Economic Advisers.

So long as total levels of output remain constant, an increase in the consumption of one group must be at the expense of another group. If aged people are given a greater share of the fixed output, everybody else gets less. This might be desirable on a number of grounds, but the preferable course of action is certainly to distribute a larger pie.

We must depend ultimately upon expansion of the output of the economy as the source of economic security for the whole population. But on both economic grounds and grounds of equity, the distribution of the output of the economy must be a matter of continuing concern.

POTENTIAL NATIONAL OUTPUT

The total volume of goods produced by the economy depends upon only two things. The first is output per worker, which in turn rests upon output per man-hour and the number of hours worked. The second is the number of workers.

Productivity

Over the long run, output per man-hour has risen by about 2.5 per cent per year. This increase has come about primarily not because workers have been more diligent on the job, but because they have had progressively more and better resources with which to work, such as improved machines and processes in factories, more investment in plant and machinery per worker, better strains of crops and animals, and better fertilizer on farms. With an increasing amount of concentration upon basic and industrial research and development, and with more widespread adoption of scientific farming technique, it is virtually certain that the long-run rate of increase in productivity will be sustained.

The effect of this increase in productivity on total output will be offset to some extent by a continuation of the long-run decline in the length of the work week. Nevertheless, the increase in productivity will be such that total output can rise despite a decline in hours worked. Over the course of a year, each worker will produce more even though he works less.

Whether the aging of the labor force in future years will increase or decrease productivity is a moot point. As other speakers have emphasized, the decline in agility and physical vigor that comes with age may be partly or totally offset by increasing experience and reliability. In any event, the aging of the population will have a relatively minor effect upon productivity.

Labor Force

The population from which the labor force is drawn will continue to increase for several decades. What proportion of this growing population will be in the labor force, that is, available to contribute to production?

This can be estimated by looking first at those who will not be in the labor force. There is the aged group. I need not expand at length here upon a primary theme of these meetings. The number of aged persons is increasing and will become a higher and higher proportion of the total population. By 1975, between 9 and 12 per cent of the population will be sixty-five years of age, or older, as contrasted with 7 per cent in 1948. It is quite likely, however, that a smaller proportion of older workers will be in the labor force in 1960 than in 1948. There has been a fairly steady and marked decline in the proportion of persons over sixty-five who are in the labor force. In 1890, for example, almost 70 per cent of the men sixty-five years of age and over were in the labor force. By 1940, this figure declined to 42 per cent, and it will probably decline to about 36 per cent in 1950. By 1960 it might fall as low as 30 per cent, but this is by no means certain.

The net result of these two factors, a rising number of aged persons combined with decreasing labor force participation of this group, may well be to keep the number of older workers in the labor force constant at about 2.3 million.

In the young population the high birth rates during the past few years have temporarily reversed a long-run reduction in the proportion of the population under fifteen years of age. In 1948, about 25 per cent of the total population is in that age bracket. But even if the birth rate remains at very high levels through 1950, less than 25 per cent of the population will be under fifteen years of age in 1975. This percentage may well fall to twenty or below.

In summary, the increase in the older group will be offset by a drop in the younger group. About the same proportion of the population will be of working age then as now. This extremely important long-run trend toward a decline in the economically dependent younger age group, which is one factor producing an aging total population, is often overlooked when attention is centered solely upon the increasing size of the older age groups.

When account is taken of other factors, such as the proportion of women between the ages of fifteen and sixty-five who will probably be working and changes in the size of the group in school, it appears likely that the proportion of the total population that will be in the labor force in 1960 and 1965 will be as large as it is now.

We are not, in short, faced within the next few decades with a rising proportion of economically dependent persons in the population. Moreover, since the total population will continue to grow, our labor force is going to expand gradually for some time to come. The labor force may reach about sixty-five million in 1960, as compared with about sixty million in 1948.

Gross National Product

As a combined result of an increase in output per worker and an expanding labor force over the next few decades, the country is clearly capable of turning out a much greater volume of goods. The gross national product could expand by 40 or 50 per cent by 1960. The money value of our national product, assuming no change in prices, could rise from $230 billion in 1947 to $320 or $350 billion in 1960. This would mean a substantial increase in per capita as well as total income.

If we take the steps necessary to ensure that this potential level of output is actually achieved, we shall have secured an economic base for a level of economic security for the whole population that is much higher than ever before in our history.

But achieving the economic base for adequate economic security will make possible, rather than ensure, economic security for the aged. Obviously, no increase in the economy's real incomes will provide adequate aid to aged nonworkers if that income is distributed only to those who participate currently in its creation.

The vital question then becomes: How shall the increasing real income of the economy be distributed? And this distribution problem is extremely controversial whether the total "pie" to be cut is large or small. The possibilities are numerous. Income may go predominantly to raising the standard of living of the workers and savers responsible for its creation. Or a larger share of total real income may go to those who are not currently producing, of whom older persons are but one group. Total real income may even be deliberately reduced in return for increased leisure in the form of a shorter working day or work week, or longer annual vacations.

These choices will not be dictated or set by any master plan. They will evolve out of people's attitudes toward work, out of their sense of responsibility for their children and for older persons, out of thousands of collective bargaining agreements, out of an infinitely complex set of economic and social forces.

This does not mean that foresight and planning for the future are either futile or pernicious. We can and should take what we know, make judgments of values, and propose a course of action. The first step in defining some sound economic principles to be followed in planning for an aging population is to assess the institutions, laws, and customs that now exist for provision of economic security to older persons.

MEANS OF PROVIDING ECONOMIC SECURITY TO AGED PERSONS

The means by which part of the product of the economy is provided to older persons can be conveniently divided between those involving private action — individual and group — and those involving governmental action. A brief review of both private and governmental means of ensuring economic security to older persons will indicate the strengths and weaknesses of the total array of devices that we have to deal with this problem.

Private Action

Security through work. For older persons who want to work and who can work, continuing employment is the most satisfying means of securing an income so far as the individual is concerned and the most productive so far as the economy is concerned.

Most older workers do not retire because they wish to stop working. They are unable to keep up the pace required on jobs available to them, or employers feel that they are not as productive as younger workers. Surveys of men receiving federal old-age benefits in 1940 showed that only about one in twenty stopped work voluntarily while he was in good health. About a third retired because they were in poor health, because work had become too hard, and for similar reasons. But more than half of them had been discharged.

If past trends continue, it is clear that enforced retirement is going to be the lot of a constantly increasing proportion of older workers. As I have indicated, as few as 30 per cent of the men who will be over sixty-five in 1960 — as compared with about 40 per cent in 1948 — may be in the labor force.

Such a development would mean a progressive reduction in the proportion of older persons who would engage in productive work and a relatively sharp increase in the number dependent upon their own savings or upon others for support.

There are strong forces acting toward a constant decline in participation of older workers in the labor force. Such factors as increasing mechanization of industry and a relative decline in the importance of agricultural employment and self-employment may continue to squeeze older workers out of employment.

But the proportion of older workers in the labor force will continue to decline sharply only if the total demand for manpower is less than the number of people who want to work. In a full employment economy, as we saw during the war, age in itself is not a barrier to employment. Full employment now and in the future will mean jobs for all aged persons who choose to work — even those whose productivity is quite low. There are still about one million more men over the age of sixty-five at work than there would be if prewar trends had continued.

Only by maintaining full employment can older workers who are willing and able to work be assured of jobs and retirement be made a matter of free choice. As is true of so many aspects of our national life, sustained maximum employment and output will mean a sharp reversal in historical trends in the work history of older workers.

But if substantial unemployment develops, prejudice and the pressure of costs will again militate against older workers. The outlook is bleak for sustaining the employment of older workers solely by exhortation of employers and by pointing out how rough enforced idleness is on older workers.[2]

The terms of public measures for providing income to older workers can, of course, be an active force in influencing the number of old people who continue to work.

So far as the labor market is concerned, it would be

[2] In Chapter IX, Dr. Clague discusses employability and the conditions of more employment for older people.

advisable to minimize the number of old persons in retirement when production and employment are at high levels. In such a situation — looking for the moment only at economic considerations — every aged worker who retires decreases levels of output. Relatively low pensions combined with eligibility conditions that would permit aged persons to earn unlimited amounts without sacrificing their pension rights would cause a higher proportion of older workers to remain in the labor force.

But during periods of heavy unemployment, it would be advisable to encourage as many older workers as possible to leave the labor market. Retirement would be maximized if high pensions were provided with the stipulation that any earnings would cause the retired person to lose his pension.

It is clear, however, that considerations other than effects upon the size of the labor force must determine the size of benefits and the conditions under which they will be paid. Since old-age benefits are financed by contributions, they could not be arbitrarily juggled in response to labor market conditions. Moreover, the primary function of the benefits is to provide a decent livelihood to older workers, and not to establish a system for expanding and contracting the labor force. Benefits should not be cut because it would be desirable to increase output by expanding the labor force. Even though it might be desirable to let retired workers earn unlimited amounts without sacrificing benefit rights during prosperous periods, the increase in benefit costs must be taken into account.

In summary, the effect of the terms of old-age and survivors' insurance should be influenced to a relatively minor degree by general labor market policies.

Private savings and current income. The adoption of the Social Security Act marked acceptance of the proposition that few individual workers will, even if they can, save enough during their working lives to support themselves during retirement. Another assumption underlying the act was that friends and relatives of aged people would not devote an adequate share of current income to the aged if each family had to bear the cost of caring for its own elder members by unplanned contributions.

This does not mean that individuals will not continue to save for their old age, nor that families will not continue to provide for aged relatives out of current income. The basic income provided by old-age benefits will never be adequate for those older people who have been in the middle and upper income brackets.

There is every prospect that individuals' savings to provide for income after retirement — in the form of insurance or otherwise — will continue to grow. It is also probable that as the population ages, individuals will voluntarily devote a substantial proportion of income to provision for old age even if the social insurance programs are markedly expanded.

Private group pension plans. The growth of private group pension plans — employer, union, and joint plans — since the Social Security Act was adopted has been substantial. There are now about six million workers covered by these plans, including the recently adopted miners' plan. Only about two and one-half million workers, excluding that were absorbed into the public railroad retirement plan, were covered in 1935.

Labor organizations have become increasingly aware of the long-run growth of the aged group and of the effects of industrial employment policy on work opportunities for older workers. Management has become more concerned over the challenge that would be presented to the free enterprise system if wage and employment policies left an increasing number of persons without a decent livelihood. The Social Security Act itself generated interest in and dramatized the problems presented by an aging population. Finally, wage stabilization during the war and tax law revisions that encouraged the establishment of reserves for old-age pensions by private employers stimulated the adoption of pension plans.

As is true of private savings, it is entirely likely that private group pension plans will continue to expand. During recent years, the inadequacy of governmental old-age pensions has undoubtedly contributed to the growth of industrial pension plans. But futher expansion can be expected even after old-age benefits are substantially expanded.

It would be unfortunate, however, if the existence of these private plans were to serve as an effective argument against expansion of social insurance. Private plans can never approach universal coverage. Since they are private plans, their continued existence is not certain. Benefits are contingent upon continued employment with a specific employer, rather than upon a lifework history.

Moreover, the effect of widespread private pension plans upon the re-employment of older workers deserves serious attention. Many plans are so designed that employers are reluctant to hire older workers because of the potential pension costs involved.

As a supplement to basic security through social insurance, private pension plans are highly desirable; as a substitute they would be completely inadequate.

Private charity. The relative role of private charity as a means of providing economic security to older workers will probably decline gradually.

The expansion of devices for providing income to older workers as a matter of right rather than as a matter of charity will reduce the proportion of older people who will be forced to rely upon private charity. In addition, the increasing proportion of consumers' incomes that will be devoted to the care of the aged through savings, industrial pensions plans, and social insurance will leave a smaller burden for private charity.

Nevertheless, many individuals and groups, such as churches and fraternal organizations, will be willing to supplement basic old-age security measures by private charity.

Governmental Action

I have talked thus far primarily of private means, individual and group, of providing economic security to the aged. Let us turn now to those measures that involve governmental action. These are of two kinds; first, the national old-age and survivors' insurance system, under which payments related to prior earnings are paid as a matter of right to eligible aged and financed by compulsory contributions dedicated to old-age benefits; second, the state old-age assistance payments — granted on the basis of a means test to needy aged persons to the extent permitted by general revenues appropriated for this purpose by the state and Federal governments.

Before discussing these two programs, I should like to outline a problem that underlies all decisions relating to the scope of both old-age insurance and old-age assistance. This is the problem of designing public programs so that various groups in the population are treated equitably.

If a given proportion of the gross national product is to be distributed through governmental payments to individuals, there is a limit to the amount that can go to each group. This creates some difficult problems of public policy. They can be illustrated by reference to three groups — the aged, the disabled, and children.

Under the existing old-age and survivors' insurance law, no worker who is permanently and totally disabled is entitled to draw benefits until he reaches the age of sixty-five. This clearly imposes severe hardships upon younger disabled persons, for disabling sickness and accidents often occur when family responsibilities are heavy and savings are low.

On the other hand, many persons have argued that since benefits under this law are an earned right, paid for by prior contributions, a worker who reaches the age of sixty-five should be allowed to draw a full benefit whether he continues to work or not. Now benefits are denied when earnings in any month exceed $15.

The force of both contentions cannot be denied. But if disability benefits were adopted and if benefits to aged persons were paid regardless of the level of current earnings, benefit costs would be more than people would be willing to contribute to this program. Therefore, under present conditions a choice must be made. In this case, it is fairly clear that the need of a totally disabled person is greater than the need of an aged worker who can still hold down a job.

The problem of allocating resources most efficiently arises in acute form when the needs of children are compared with those of older persons. When the consequences of inadequate diet and poor education for children are compared with the consequences of inadequate income for older persons, the thought that the next order of business should be more extensive aid for children inevitably arises.

These considerations of equity are, as I see it, the basic objection to proposals like the Townsend Plan. There are, in addition, some fallacies in the economic reasoning often advanced to support the plan which I shall discuss in a few minutes.

This problem of balancing equities is ever present when changes in the social security program are under consideration. A realistic, equitable program for aid to aged persons cannot be built solely by examining the needs of older people. Decisions that in themselves appear callous and inequitable often take on a different light when the relative economic needs of all groups are taken into account. And the relative needs of all groups must be considered because the basic problem — to repeat — is the manner in which the whole national product is to be distributed among the whole population so as to maximize social welfare and the national output. The following discussion is set in the light of this general guide.

Old-age and survivors' insurance. The federal old-age and survivors' insurance system is completely inadequate as a means of providing basic economic security in old age.

Old-age insurance, theoretically the first line of defense against economic insecurity of older workers, is now actually less important than old-age assistance. About $90 million a month is now being disbursed as old-age assistance payments; payments under the old-age and survivors' insurance program now total only about $45 million a month and only $33 million of this goes to aged persons. About one and one-half million aged persons are receiving old-age insurance payments; about two and four-tenths million persons are receiving old-age assistance payments.

This distortion is created by a number of serious gaps in the old-age and survivors' insurance program. About twenty-five million persons — two out of very five in the labor force — do not work in jobs covered by the act. The benefits paid are grossly inadequate. The average payment to a retired recipient was $24 a month—$288 a year. Recent studies show that an elderly couple needs an income of at least $1,700 a year to support a modest but adequate level of living. It is clear that current benefits are too low to provide even a substantial part of the income required to support an aged couple at a reasonably adequate level of living.

Coverage should be broadly extended so that most workers will have substantial benefit rights when they retire. The administrative problems that necessitated exclusion of such large groups as agricultural workers and self-employed persons have been solved.

The benefit formula should be readjusted so that the average benefit will increase by at least 50 per cent. Both the minimum and the maximum payments should be increased. Beneficiaries should be permitted to earn at least $40 a month — rather than $15 — without sacrificing the insurance payments, and beneficiaries over seventy years of age should be permitted to earn unlimited amounts without sacrificing their pensions.

The limit on taxable earnings should be raised from $3,000 to $4,800 a year. This increase will both lift the wage base upon which benefits are computed and increase the income of the trust fund.

When benefits are raised, the contributions of both workers and employers should be increased from 1 per cent to 1.5 per cent. Under a contributory social insurance system, every major change in benefit rights should be matched by a change in contributions reflecting the cost of the increase.

These major deficiencies of the system have been exhaustively studied by the executive and legislative branches of the Federal Government, and by competent private groups. There is a broad area of agreement as to the steps that should be taken immediately. These are the next steps. Further changes will have to be considered as economic and social conditions evolve.

In future years, as the number of beneficiaries and benefit rights per beneficiary increase, benefit outlays will exceed 3 per cent of payrolls. By the year 2000, the annual cost of benefits may range between 6 and 10 per cent of payrolls, if changes such as those outlined above were adopted. But payroll taxes should not be relied upon to cover fully the cost of a comprehensive old-age benefit program. When annual outgo exceeds the income from a 3 per cent payroll tax, it might be wise to increase the payroll tax to 4 per cent to preserve the contributory nature of the system. Any costs above that level should, however, be covered by a contribution from general revenue. Indefinite increases in payroll taxes for this and other kinds of social insurances would have an adverse effect on the economy. The nation as a whole has an interest in the welfare of the aged, and substantial benefit payments will reduce the burden imposed upon the general taxpayer by old-age assistance.

Old-age assistance. While the old-age assistance and old-age insurance programs are now completely out of balance, the answer does not lie in curtailment of public assistance. Even with an expanded old-age insurance program, there will always be substantial numbers of aged persons who will require additional income. The relatively smaller group who will need old-age assistance in the future should be adequately provided for.

The current federal-state old-age assistance program contains a number of basic defects.

The financing provisions are defective because the amount which the Federal Government will grant to a state approximates the amount which the state provides for old-age assistance. While the federal grants are a somewhat higher proportion of the state appropriation in those states with relatively low per capita income, the federal grant program does not give adequate weight to wide variations in the economic and fiscal capacity of the states. States with relatively low per capita income simply cannot afford to provide the money necessary to support adequate old-age assistance payments. The answer to this problem is to increase the proportion of total old-age assistance costs that will be borne by the Federal Government in those states with relatively low per capita income. This principle should, moreover, apply to all federal public assistance grants.

A second defect in the old-age assistance program is that the Federal Government will match no part of any payment over $45 a month per aged person. Beginning October 1, 1948, this amount is to be increased to $50 in accordance with a law passed by Congress at the last session. But an elderly couple needs from $120 to $150 a month, depending upon the place of residence, to support a minimum standard of living. Some thirty states have therefore found it necessary, because of rising living costs, to set the maximum payments per aged needy person well above $50 a month. To assist states in meeting this burden, the maximum payment toward which the Federal Government will contribute should be increased to $60 a month. But this increase would be unwise unless more adequate federal aid is given to the low income states and unless the old-age insurance plan is strengthened at the same time.

Finally, federal public assistance grants should be available to help finance payments to any needy person whom states find eligible for public assistance. It has become clear over the past few years that restriction of federal aid to three categories of persons — the needy aged, the needy blind, and needy dependent children — has induced states to be relatively generous with these persons and relatively niggardly with others in equal need.

Such a change in the structure of public assistance might well retard the rate at which public assistance payments to the aged will increase. But there is ample evidence that the needy aged have, despite the absolute inadequacy of public assistance payments to them, been relatively better treated than other needy groups.

If we look again at the principle that the requirements of all needy groups should be balanced against one another, that the income supplied to all needy groups must be related to the capacity of the economy, and that the contributory old-age insurance system should become the backbone of public measures providing economic security to the aged, it is evident that a thorough overhauling of both old-age insurance and public assistance is needed. There is a clear and present danger that the contributory social insurance program will be engulfed by public assistance.

SOME ECONOMIC CONSEQUENCES OF PROVIDING SECURITY TO OLDER PERSONS

The total of payments to older workers through all of these private and governmental devices is going to rise over the years in both absolute and relative size as the aged population increases. Such a redistribution of income will have economic consequences of the first magnitude. Without attempting to exhaust this topic, I should like to point out the magnitude involved, and some of the major factors that will have to be taken into account if the economic burden of caring for the aged is to be minimized.

The Direct Money Cost of Economic Security for the Aged

While it is impossible to state with any degree of precision the total income supplied to older persons not in the labor force, some rough calculations that indicate nothing more than orders of magnitude can be made.

If persons over sixty-five years of age who are not in the labor market had in 1947 the same per capita income as the population as a whole, their total income — counting both goods and services — would total about $12 billion or about 5 per cent of the gross national product. It is quite possible, however, that their total income was only $9 or $10 billion. No one knows.

We do know that less than $2 billion was supplied by public measures. Hence, private efforts — group and individual — are still the primary source of economic security for aged people who are not in the labor market.

By 1960, assuming full production and employment, expanded public programs, and substantial growth in the aged population, it is entirely possible that $25 billion will be supplied to older persons. Even this sum would leave substantial numbers of older persons in need. It seems likely, moreover, that the major burden of caring for older persons will continue to be carried by private efforts even if the old-age pensions and assistance are markedly expanded.

In this connection it should be pointed out that to a large but indeterminate extent, public payments are merely a substitute for support that would be provided from private sources — friends, relatives, and private charities — if the public payments were not made. To a substantial degree, public payments to the aged are merely a change in the channels through which support is provided. But this point should not be overemphasized. Such measures as old-age and survivors' insurance and public assistance for the aged do increase the total income of the aged as a group and distributes it more equitably among that group. Moreover, the shift in the method of financing is quite significant in itself.

If the gross national product rises to the levels that are potentially attainable — perhaps $350 billion — the rise in payments to the aged will represent about 7 per cent of the gross national product. But if, as a result of a depression or any other development, the gross national product remained at a substantially lower level, the burden of providing for the aged could be quite heavy. We see again that maintenance of maximum levels of production and employment plays a key role in determining the economic burden of the aged on the economy.

All of these rough calculations are based on the assumption that the price level in 1960 will be at about the level of 1948. I need not emphasize the shaky nature of that assumption, nor spell out the consequences that would follow either a sharp increase or a sharp decrease in prices.

The manner in which the price level determines the real value of fixed money payments to the aged has been demonstrated by price rises since 1940. The current inflation is cutting sharply into the real value of income from insurance, public and private. For example, the average old-age benefit of $24 today will purchase only 70 per cent as much as the average benefit of $24 in 1940.

The ultimate solution of this problem lies in attainment of reasonable stability in the cost of living, a problem that extends far beyond the subject of this Institute.

The immediate and pressing problem is the extent to which and the manner in which governmental payments to the aged should be revised in the light of a price level that will never return to prewar levels. I have suggested that an increase of at least 50 per cent is the minimum adjustment needed in the light of a permanently higher price level, particularly since benefits were inadequate before World War II.

Repercussions of Old-Age Security upon the Economy

The volume of payments made to older persons who are not in the labor market is merely a partial base for a discussion of the economic effects of providing economic security for the aged. The combined effects of the payments and the method of financing the payments can have varied and important repercussions upon the operation of the entire economy.

The pattern of demand for goods, for example, will obviously shift as a larger part of the total product turned out by the working population is diverted to older persons. This is true whether the transfer is through private or public channels. Housing suitable for older persons will be in greater demand. Medical facilities devoted to the care of the aged will expand markedly. Recreational facilities designed for the use of older persons will increase. But since these changes will occur gradually and imperceptibly over several decades, they will create no serious difficulties.

The effects of providing an increasing share of the nation's output to older persons upon total levels of demand and the stability of the economy are much more significant than the composition of whatever total demand may exist.

The real cost — in an economic sense — of economic security for older persons cannot be measured in terms of the amount of money provided to them. These payments, in themselves, do not necessarily involve a real cost to the community as a whole. They are merely a redistribution of income. The economic cost of the payments is more validly measured by the effects that this redistribution will have upon levels of output and employment, and upon the stability of output and employment.

To the extent, for example, that increasing concern over provision of old-age security leads to an increase in the total savings of the community — through savings accounts or through various forms of insurance or private pension plans or public reserves for social insurance — funds available for current consumption would be decreased. Moreover, it is quite possible that the funds saved would not be diverted into investment, so that total expenditures throughout the economy would fall. While this chain of consequences would be useful during inflationary periods, there might well be times when this cut could precipitate a general downward movement in production, prices, and employment. Thus, an increased volume of saving for old-age security might well necessitate compensatory measures to sustain both consumer and investment demand.

Apart from the questions raised by an increase in savings, the source of funds to pay public old-age pensions are of the greatest significance to the economy as a whole. Federal old-age benefits are now financed by payroll taxes imposed directly upon covered workers and paid on behalf of covered workers by employers. These taxes fall most heavily upon those in lower income groups, and they also tend to reduce consumption. It is entirely possible that in years to come the maintenance of economic stability at high levels will necessitate measures to bolster consumers' purchasing power so that the full product of our increasingly productive economy can be taken off the market, without a disruptive decline in prices and wages. A steady rise in payroll taxes— both for old-age benefits and for other social insurances — would run directly counter to the policies needed in such a situation.

But we can more reasonably assume that the system will be financed by a gradually increasing payroll tax, stabilized at a relatively low level — about 4 per cent of payrolls — and supplemented by a contribution from general revenues. This is the plan of financing that appears likely to develop as the old-age and survivors' insurance system matures. The redistribution of income involved in using the proceeds of a progressive income tax — the major component of federal general revenues — to provide payments to older persons who will spend their benefits currently may well counteract the depressing effect of a somewhat higher pay-roll tax.

Finally, the possible effects upon cyclical movements of expanded economic security for the older population should be mentioned.

Experience during and after the war has shown that the number of persons receiving old-age benefits is quite responsive to general economic conditions. The fact that the size of the group over sixty-five years of age is gradually increasing does not mean that the number of recipients of old-age benefits will rise steadily in every year. High levels of output will cause many older workers to delay retirement, thus increasing the size of the labor force at a time when such an increase will help to ease upward pressure on wage rates and prices. If a general decline in production and employment begins, an adequate system of old-age benefits will permit large numbers of workers to retire. Their retirement will tend to decrease the size of the labor force, thus exerting a pressure towards maintenance of wage rates and towards maintenance of full time employment and income for those remaining in the labor market. And payments of retirement benefits will tend to sustain a shrinking volume of purchasing power. These effects, while inadequate in themselves to ensure economic stability, will operate as a consistent part of a broader program.

The limited potentialities of governmental payments as a means of stabilizing the economy at high levels deserve particular emphasis. The economic theories underlying such proposals as the Townsend Plan contain fallacies that can endanger the success of our national effort to ensure sustained high levels of output and employment.

The reasoning underlying such proposals is deceptively simple and plausible. In essence, those who advance plans of this sort claim that depressions are caused by declining markets. The declining markets cause a drop in output and employment. These declines are cumulative and mutually reinforcing because fear of further contraction leads to a further restriction of spending and to contraction of output by businessmen.

On the basis of this chain of reasoning, it is held that if consumers are given money enough to sustain markets, the series of events leading to a general slump can never start. Expenditure of the newly provided funds will sustain markets, and the sustained markets will prevent a drop in production, employment, and prices.

The significant truth in this analysis is that maintenance of consumer demands can contribute substantially to levels of demand through the whole economy. Action designed to bolster consumer demand is therefore a necessary and desirable part of a general national program promoting economic stability at high levels.

But sole or even major reliance upon money payments to individuals by government as a means of preventing or mitigating depression would be a tragic error. The fundamental gap in plans of this sort is that they ignore the key role of investment levels in the maintenance of economic stability. During prosperous periods 10 to 15 per cent of our gross national product goes into investment — expansion and improvement of the nation's stock of capital goods. The volume of investment is, moreover, to a large extent independent of current and prospective levels of consumer demand. If, for example, a heavy wave of investment during a boom leaves capital needs largely met, the volume of new investment will decline even though consumer demand — current and prospective — remains high. These waves of investment demand can contribute to general upward and downward movements in the entire economy.

A sound program for evening cyclical movements therefore must include policies and measures — public and private — designed to smooth out fluctuations in every major component of the economy.

CONCLUSION

From this review of some of the economic problems posed by an aging population, it is clear that we have the institutions and customs that can serve to transfer income to aged people as the aging process continues. A combination of current earnings, personal savings, private charity, industrial insurance, public old-age pensions and public assistance provide flexible and adequate channels for providing aged persons with income. What we must do is strengthen the old-age pension and public assistance programs to give the form more substance.

But the efficacy of all of these devices rests ultimately, as I have suggested repeatedly, upon the attainment and maintenance of maximum levels of output and employment. It is this task that poses the greatest challenge to our political and economic wisdom. We are well advanced in devising means of providing income to a growing aged group. We are less advanced in diagnosing and dealing effectively with the broad forces that lead to underutilization of our material and human resources and to the "boom and bust" sequences that determine the standard of living not only of the aged but of the whole population.

XI

A Comprehensive Program for Personal and Social Adjustment in Old Age

By Harry A. Overstreet

Harry A. Overstreet is professor emeritus at the College of the City of New York, where he served as head of the Department of Philosophy and Psychology for many years. He served as research associate of the American Association for Adult Education; as a member of the Board of Trustees of Town Hall, New York, and as codirector with Mrs. Overstreet of the Leadership School at Town Hall. He is the author of many books, including Influencing Human Behavior, About Ourselves, *and* The Enduring Quest.

INTRODUCTION

I COME with deep emotion to this meeting of the Institute on Aging. I am sensible of two facts: first, that this is the Charles A. Fisher Memorial Institute, a tribute of the University of Michigan to a great man. I am grateful to the University for paying this tribute. In the second place I am sensible that in this Institute you are beginning something new, something that promises to be as significant in American adult education as anything that has yet been developed. I happened to have the pleasure this morning of listening to the two papers and was more than ever aware of the fact that here is indeed something new under the educational sun. You may remember Dr. Clague said at the end of his paper that the whole problem of adult perplexities really comes down to education, that we must learn to educate in a new way. I am happy that it is under the auspices of the Charles A. Fisher Memorial Institute that we witness the beginnings of this new kind of adult education.

The adult who has hitherto been largely unserviced in America is now to be serviced in a way hitherto untried. I am likewise particularly grateful to Mr. Soop for what

179

he said about the connection of my wife and me with Dr. Fisher's thinking. We had many talks about adults; Dr. Fisher was constantly stressing in those talks his high conception of adulthood and his feeling that we had somehow missed helping adults to bring their adulthood to a fine climax of maturity. We had, so he felt, by our indifference to the needs of the grown-up years, let adults level off into a kind of futile dullness. His passionate conviction was that adulthood could be the best time of life and that it had powers in it that had not as yet been realized by our culture. His ambition was to put into this University and into America the kind of education that would help adults to move into a triumphant maturity of life.

I call to mind that Dr. Fisher established last year the first course for the aging that has ever been given in the University — a course of sixteen weeks, not, primarily, for adults already on the tottering edge, but for adults still full of vigor, who wanted to learn how to make themselves ready for the retirement time of life and to have an enriched time while they were on their way. The great need of our time, he always felt, was to take the fear out of adult life; to make adults feel that the movement into retirement would be not into futility and apologetic defeat but into a happy and productive maturity. It is perhaps symbolic of the way a man's work continues that this particular class was in session on the evening of Dr. Fisher's death.

I remember the many talks that Dr. Fisher, Mrs. Fisher, Mr. and Mrs. Soop, and my wife and I had about all these things. Out of those talks and out of Dr. Fisher's original thinking this "new thing under the sun" has come.

I am asked today to talk about a comprehensive program. Much of what I am going to say will be in terms of what we talked about in former days. I have the feeling, with Dr. Fisher, that a comprehensive program must be one that will make the movement through adulthood not an anticlimax but a mounting satisfaction.

EDUCATION FOR ADULTHOOD

I should like to think of this program as a kind of new gospel we are bringing to the adults of America. They have been the neglected group of our American culture. We have had a curious habit of idealizing immaturity. Think of the many ways in which we do that: "Backward, turn backward, O Time, in your flight, Make me a child again just for tonight!" The assumption is that childhood is the best time of life. As a matter of fact we have idealized immaturity so much that we adults are afraid of our children.[1] Parents are afraid to hold their children to high standards lest their children think them old fogies. Advertisers have stressed immaturity. They have convinced us that it is a dreadful thing to have wrinkles — that we must buy their particular cream, or soap, or lotion, or what not, to cover up the fact that we are really adult.

There is another and far more hurtful way in which our culture has overstressed immaturity. Its greatest enterprise — that of education — is given over almost entirely to the development of the immature. We spend vast sums of money, building up an imposing system of education, thinking always of children, always of youth. We have not in comparable measure paid attention to adult needs. Hence adults have largely been left in the lurch. They have been left economically in the lurch, since they do not know what is going to happen to them when they are beyond the earning stage, or what they can do about it. They are left educationally in the lurch, for it is only in rare cases that we find even meager educational opportunities for adults. What is happening now is that we are beginning to realize that there are many things adults need to know and to do, even in their early adulthood, if their maturing years are to be a mounting satisfaction.

As a matter of fact, adulthood is the first time in the individual's life when he can really look at life with mature eyes. Think of how the child looks at life. A child cannot

[1] Dr. Burgess discusses this point in Chapter I.

understand much; cannot know much. The child is largely helpless. Consider how the adolescent looks at life. He looks at it through a haze of uncritical enthusiasms and unsettling bewilderments. He is by no means able as yet to see life steadily and wholly. Only when the person grows into adulthood has he at least a chance for a mature look at life. Yet when the average adult comes to the point where he can have this mature look at life, he usually lets go; settles down; stops growing; becomes a "mere" adult.

In this Institute the thought is paramount that adults need to learn the art of becoming truly adult. Or, less cryptically, adults need to learn the art of becoming mature. While everyone who manages to grow up becomes adult, not everyone who becomes adult becomes a mature adult. Adulthood that is not mature — that is still arrested in development — that still holds childish or adolescent attitudes and points of view — cannot be a triumph of life.[2]

What this Institute is aiming at, then, is to discover how to steer adults away from an immature toward a mature adulthood. How can this be done?

I should like to imagine a situation. Suppose a sizable group of adults were to ask themselves the question: "How can we make our adulthood move toward maturity?" what would their answer be likely to be?

KNOWING OURSELVES AND OTHERS

Today we have the chance to know ourselves in ways we have never been able to before. The first thing, I suppose, that any such adult group would want to know would be about themselves as individuals. They would want to know about their physical selves — how to keep in good shape and how to grow in vigor. But in this psychological age they would want to know also about their mental, emotional, and social selves.

Suppose a group should start trying to discover these things. As a matter of fact, almost no group in America tries

2 See Dr. Stieglitz' similar comment in Chapter III.

to do this. All over our land there are practically no adults who, in company with fellow adults, try to find out what is discoverable about themselves. Yet this is the most important knowledge they need to possess. Most of our gravest problems, in individual and social life, root in misunderstanding of our psychosomatic and psychosocial selves. Members of a group like this would decide that to know themselves — as they now, in this psychological age, are able to know themselves — should be their first adult job of continuing education.

The second thing such a group would want to know would come out of the realization, a realization that their new-found psychological knowledge will have given them, of the profound effect that environment has upon people. The speakers talked this morning about the work environment and how it breeds in numberless adults an overmastering fear of their old age. This is only one of the many environments that make adult life a triumph or a defeat.

Thus, the next job of this group of adults would be to get a true insight into the community environment in which they live. What does this community environment do to them, to their children, and to their fellowmen? Does it build in them habits of mature relationships or encourage immature relationships? To know their community environment would come next in importance to knowing their individual selves.

Most adults take their community environment for granted and so permit themselves to be victimized by all kinds of forces that hold them back from a full maturing. These adults of ours, on the contrary, would move about with critical, psychological eyes, appraising their community environment in terms of what it does to encourage or discourage growth into fullness of life.

Most adults have the power to influence the growth of children. They may be teachers, employers, ministers, or just parents. The third project, I think, the group of adults would want to undertake would be to look back upon their own childhood and estimate how wisely or unwisely they were influenced in their growing years. These adults should now be able to see with the eyes of their adulthood, and with those eyes they should be able to discover things that ought not to have been done to them, or to any children, and things that were left undone. In brief, they should now, as adults, be able to review their bringing up in home, school, and community and appraise the good and the bad. In this effort at appraisal the group would invite in psychologists, educators, anthropologists, sociologists, and other scientists — as they would in all their projects.

Men and women who, in their adult years, thus looked at the whole educative process with mature eyes would achieve a significance in their own right. Unlike the average adult, who never examines the educative process with a critical intelligence and who is therefore as likely as not to be a mere repository of educational platitudes and intolerances, these adults would achieve the distinction of an intelligent attitude toward the upbringing and educating of children. They would, therefore, in their adult years, be proper partners in this central enterprise of life. Thus, their adult years would have a significance that the years of the average adult seldom achieve. Through their mature insight into the education and rearing of the young, they would have the authority of a grown-up wisdom.

A fourth project. We were trying this morning to understand how the economic system could be related to the sound health of the adult. We decided that in many respects the economic system was badly out of relation to a sound adulthood. Too many adults have not enough to live on when they grow old; too many have to live with relatives; and so on. The whole question, then, of how we can gear an economic system to adults in such ways that the adults will be kept happily growing revealed itself as a most urgent problem of our culture. Our adult group would want to study the economic order; would want not to take it for granted; not to damn it uncritically, but to try to discover how an economic order could be contrived that would be good for the sound maturing of life.[3]

In the fifth place, the adult group would want to have something more than the half-illusory, disconnected, and often mischievous social and political information they find in the newspapers. A notable survey was carried on at the University of Michigan two years ago to find the extent to which the average American adult understood the political issues of the day — specifically, in this case, the issues of the atomic bomb and of our relations with Russia. The findings were a sad commentary upon both the ignorance and the indifference of our newspaper-made minds.

If adults are to be really significant in their adult years, they will need to grow up to the maturity of intelligent judgment on public affairs. As makers of public opinion, they will need to be more than contributors to a pooled ignorance. Thus, this group will want to give themselves the chance to understand their social and political world as they need to understand it if they are to build a responsible public opinion.

Finally, the group will want to find their way understandingly into the great human tradition. Most of us know very little about that tradition. We are heirs to it, but most of us know very little of what we have inherited. We may be able to quote a line or two from Shakespeare and even know that there was a man called Socrates. But as to our taking on the richness and potency of the human tradition, our culture has not yet done well by us. In the schools, we get the tradition when we are still too young to understand and appreciate; when we grow old enough to understand and appreciate, we are kept too preoccupied with the struggle to survive to try to make the tradition our own. This greatest source of our life's enrichment is left by most of us unappropriated. The group we have been describing will not wish this to continue. They will want to find their way into the great human tradition, drawing from it their

[3] See Chapter X for a discussion of the problems of adequate financial support.

sense of beauty, truth, and mature intention. They will plan to do this not for a month, or a year, but for decades of their life.

Already it should appear that this program we have been describing is not for a month, or a year, but for decades of adult life. This is the insight we need to achieve — the insight our culture has thus far entirely missed. We have no trouble in conceiving a span of education for our children — of eight years, twelve years, sixteen years, even twenty years or more. But as yet we have not come to see that in adulthood there must likewise be a continuing span of education. To think of a fragmentary adult course, or of several fragmentary courses, as enough is to fail utterly to understand what adulthood needs. Adults need to keep on growing. They can only keep on growing as year after year they enrich themselves with the knowledge they need to possess and to use.

We have touched on six kinds of knowledge adults need to possess and use: knowledge of themselves as psychophysical and psychosocial beings; knowledge of their community environment; knowledge of the educative processes; knowledge of the economic order; knowledge of public affairs; knowledge of their cultural inheritance. This project of adult learning can be no fly-by-night affair. It must be a lifetime project. It should be so conceived by adults themselves, and by the educational institutions that seek to serve them.

LIFETIME EDUCATION AND PARTICIPATION

Thus when today I speak of a comprehensive program for adults I mean a program of lifelong education: one that should properly begin in early adulthood and continue to the last day of our lives. This, too, was Dr. Fisher's thought: a truly comprehensive program for adults must be a continuing program. To be sure, the years of our lives are all too short for us to learn all we need to learn. But we do ill if, knowing that we cannot learn everything, we content ourselves with learning nothing. So likewise, our educational institutions do ill if, knowing that they cannot offer adults all that they need for a lifetime of growing, offer mere scraps and tidbits.

Adult education must have, not its five-year plan, but its lifetime plan of learning. For when the effort of the mind to grow into new knowledge and new insights ceases, the mind ceases. The growing adult becomes then the fixated and settled adult; the pattern of an arrested development.

The foregoing program has envisaged what the adult needs to learn. A comprehensive program should envisage likewise what he needs to do. Having savored the human tradition, our pioneering group will have caught the flair of creativeness. They themselves will want to create music, drama, story, painting, sculpture, woodwork, and so on. They will want the triumphant experience of turning their inner sense of beauty and significance into some outer form. They will want to make the word become flesh. This practice of creating is one of the experiences that Dr. Fisher's course for the aging has richly afforded its members.

Second, our adults will want to practice obligations. Knowing the human tradition, they will know how deeply they are in debt to the past and to their human fellows. They will want to pay back even a little for what they have received. Thus every one of them, singly or in company with his friends, will want to practice the obligation of doing something to better his world.

Third, they will want to practice research. Most adults, in the great matters of human concern, never practice research. Most of them skim the surfaces of our human problems, becoming surface minds with surface dogmatisms. These adults of ours will seek — each on his own — to take an area of life's problems and apply their minds with the thoroughness and exactitude that signify minds at work. One such experience of true research would make their surface thinking tame by comparison.

Finally, they will want to practice sociability and play. The fine arts of sociability and play are largely lost in adult life. Earning a living and keeping up with the Joneses have turned them into a triviality or an anxious burden. Our adults will want to recover for themselves the wisdom expressed in Masefield's line: "The hours that make us happy make us wise." Being happy with other people is a way of being wise. Being happy in the fine unseriousness of play can be a way of being wise. Our adults, having in the deepest ways learned to know one another and having learned to like being together, will seek ways in which they can practice sociability and play.

PREPARATION FOR RETIREMENT

We are only beginning to learn that laissez faire applied to adult growth into maturity, like laissez faire in other relations of life, just does not work. Adults have to plan, and be helped to plan, for the full and rich development of their lives. They have to plan early in their adult years. I have been much interested of late in talking to a number of businessmen who have been on the way to retiring and in finding them concerned about what they might best do in the years of their retirement. The consensus among them has been that they must not wait until the eve of retirement. They must begin now, with years still ahead of them. There has been among them the feeling that if they begin now to do the things that bring interest and richness into their present adulthood, they will have a dependable richness for the years of their retirement.

Brother Lawrence, you will remember, called his book *The Practice of the Presence of God.* I think this Institute is envisaging a way of life that might be phrased in a similar manner. It is envisaging the practice of the enjoyment of maturity. All these things we have talked about are ways of practicing and enjoying maturity. When we start learning about ourselves, we are practicing and enjoying the experience of maturing. When we try with our adult minds to appraise our community environments, our educational practices, our economic order, our public affairs, our whole human culture, we are practicing and enjoying the experience of maturing.

The launching of this Institute should, I feel, be looked upon as a historic event. It marks a new sense of what is needed in adult life; and a new effort to fulfill that need. The next few decades ought to see the strong development of this movement to give adults the chance so to bring their potentialities to realization that their adulthood, instead of being a time of what the psychologist, William Sheldon, has called a "dying back of the brain," is a time of the mind's greater triumph. This was Dr. Fisher's vision. It was his "good news" for his fellow adults.

Index

191